SONNETᴜ ᴛᴜ HUMAN BEINGS

AND OTHER SELECTED WORKS

by CARMEN TAFOLLA

SANTA FE
Literacy
Symposium

Courtesy of
Scott Foresman

SONNETS TO HUMAN BEINGS

AND OTHER SELECTED WORKS

by CARMEN TAFOLLA

Edited by
Ernesto Padilla

McGraw-Hill, Inc.
College Custom Series

New York St. Louis San Francisco Auckland Bogotá
Caracas Lisbon London Madrid Mexico Milan Montreal
New Delhi Paris San Juan Singapore Sydney Tokyo Toronto

Acknowledgements:

From *Arriba* Magazine, "An Interview with Carmen Tafolla" by Teresa Paloma Acosta. Copyright © 1983 by *Arriba* Magazine. Reprinted by permission of the author.

From *European Perspectives on Hispanic Literature of the United States*, "Code-Switching as Metaphor in Chicano Poetry" by Cardelia Candelaria. Copyright © 1988 by Arte Público Press. Reprinted by permission of the author and the publisher.

From *Dictionary of Literary Biography*, "Carmen Tafolla" by Yolanda Broyles González. Copyright © 1990 by Yolanda Broyles González. Reprinted by permission of the author.

From *English in Texas*, "Poetess of the New Promesa: An Interview with Carmen Tafolla" by Ann L. Jensen. Copyright © 1982 by Ann L. Jensen. Reprinted by permission of the author.

From *Teachers*, "Empowering Students Through Creative Writing", by Carmen Tafolla. Copyright © 1990 by Carmen Tafolla. Reprinted by permission of the author.

From *Five Poets of Aztlán:* "La Isabela de Guadalupe y el Apache Mío Cid," "Memories," "At the Very Last Battle," "Loca," "Como un pajarito," "La Malinche," "Si escuchas el viento...," "Caminitos," "Los Corts (5 Voices)," "Esa casa ya no existe," "And When I Dream Dreams..." by Carmen Tafolla. Copyright © 1985 by Bilingual Press/Editorial Bilingüe. Reprinted by permission of the author and the publisher.

SONNETS TO HUMAN BEINGS
AND OTHER SELECTED WORKS *by* CARMEN TAFOLLA

1 2 3 4 5 6 7 8 9 0 BKM BKM 9 0 9 8 7 6 5

ISBN 0-07-063300-2

College Custom Series Editor: Julie Kehrwald
Cover Painting: Rebozo Rojo, copyright © 1992 by Catalina Garate
Back Cover Photo: Hector de la Garza
Cover Design: Mayela Padilla, copyright © 1992
Book Design: Carol Ring
Printer/Binder: Bookmart Press

Acknowledgements from the Editor

Carmen Tafolla and Ernesto Bernal and their children Marilinda and Israel, a special thank you for being the inspiring family that you are. This volume is a dedication to humanism, a special expression of love, and, Carmen, I hope that all the world will hear your sonnets.

Thank you also to my very much loved wife, Yolanda, and children, Mayela, Gabriela, Santiago. Thank you to my mother, Tomasa Padilla, and my father, Eduardo (Lalo) Padilla.

A warm thank you to the many people at Santa Monica College who helped make the first edition of this book possible.

And a special thanks to Julie Kehrwald, Clint Kruger, and the people at McGraw-Hill who believed in the magic and power of this work, and who contributed to the beauty of this second edition.

Contents

II. SELECTED POEMS

Preface

Most of us have come to appreciate and love the vernacular poetry that has taken its place of prominence in late Twentieth Century American literature, but Carmen Tafolla's work will cause us to re-examine once again our standards and expectations. This is a poetry of voice, dialogue, and the vernacular, but it is also "heteroglossic," as professor Rosaura Sánchez has said: "Its dialogical, bilingual, and bidialectal discourses enable the poetic voice to be heteroglossic." This preface merely suggests the historical context that has led to Carmen Tafolla's startling evocation of the synchronic reality of the Chicano. There is need for more careful scholarship on the heteroglossic nature of literature, and Chicano literature in particular.

Carmen Tafolla is a poet of "voice." We get the feeling that we are walking around in the barrio, and we are delighted to meet such interesting people, who talk to us as if we were old friends. They *are* old friends by the power of magic, the magic of great literature. One doesn't need to be Chicano or Latino to identify with these characters. They are our grandmothers, our aunts, our neighbors, our friends. Here is the "blab of the pave" that Whitman had called for in *Leaves of Grass*. Here is a "selection of language really used by men," "the great and simple affections," the "naked and simple" language that Wordsworth called for in his preface to the *Lyrical Ballads*. Note that the call for the vernacular goes back far beyond both Whitman and Wordsworth: Joachim Du Bellay, in his *Defense et Illustration de la Langue Française* (1549), argued that poets should eschew Latin and write in their national language. Certainly it is true that Du Bellay would probably have been shocked by the increasing vernacularization by writers such as Wordsworth, Whitman, Alice Walker (*The Color Purple*), Toni Morrison (*The Bluest Eye*), and Tafolla, but this slide toward the appreciation of the common as the best source to commonality is logical and inevitable.

The humility in Tafolla's characters and narrators is both inspiring and deceptive. Inspiring because these characters speak on our behalf and in the process push us to epiphany, to illumination. Deceptive because (as Tafolla herself has often asserted) "these are the voices of the people" and not "crafted" art. This disavowal of deliberateness is an age-old claim going back as far as Chaucer. See, for example, the prologue to "The Franklin's Tale" in *The Canterbury Tales* where the Franklin says, "Colours ne knowe I noon, withouten drede / But swiche colours as growen in the mede," which translates into something like "without doubt I know no colors except such colors as grow in the meadow." In other words, "I tell this story through no skill of my own. I simply report the 'colours' that I perceive." But, we as readers are not deceived: we ask with Marcus Aurelius, "What is it in itself?" and answer that, clearly, this poetry of voice, this "blab of the pave" is a highly crafted work of dense aesthetics. The more simple it appears, the more we realize the beauty of an eye that reports the "colours" of the meadow.

In addition to being a poet and fiction writer, Carmen Tafolla is a charismatic presence on the stage. Her one-woman dramatization of her stories and poetry is powerfully moving. Over the past ten years, she has delighted audiences throughout the southwest with living characters, with rich vernacular, with memorable lines, with witty humor. She becomes her characters, and her characters are often the simple people of her barrio or the members of the other world with which they come in contact, such as the professor in the delightful "Quality Literature." Her characters are people with humility, people with a strong sense of identity, people who laugh at themselves, people who love and savor the world about them, people who grow and understand.

Indeed, her readings are so pleasurable that audiences crowd around her and buy up all of her books. *Curandera*, her most popular collection of poetry, has gone through three editions. Both have sold out within a year, a feat quite unusual for a collection of poetry. Lalo Press published the second and third editions of *Curandera* and was considering issuing another printing; however, it made more sense to publish Tafolla's new, award winning manuscript *Sonnets to Human Beings* (first prize in the 1989 University of California at Irvine National Chicano Literature contest). But what about Tafolla's immensely popular books of poetry and children's literature (all out of print)? Our solution was to provide a master volume, including both *Sonnets to Human Beings* and selected poems and stories from her previous books. In addition, this volume includes the critical articles that indicate the well-earned appreciation of great oral/vernacular poetry, the appreciation of original humor.*

Lest we categorize Tafolla as solely vernacular, it is important to note that she can also create poetry with a more classical outline. Often, her poetry goes beyond the simple folk, beyond the rich oral/vernacular voice. Her poetry can be dense with the more traditional rhetorical device and prosody, as is evident in the sonnets. These sonnets are incomparable in that they illustrate mastery of the technical (prosodic) conventions while turning the Elizabethan (Petrarchan) "romantic" love conventions into expansive expressions of love for humanity, into offers to immortalize, not just one's loved one, but the earth, its people, its cultures. There is beauty here, folks, there is beauty: see especially the haunting sonnet, "How Shall I Tell You." The prosody in these sonnets (as well as in the highly crafted vernacular poetry) is impeccable. The classical aesthetic is not a recent venture for Tafolla, whose poem "Voyage," written in 1975 and published in numerous American literature anthologies, carries the timeless imprint of classical form.

This volume contains critical articles by a range of scholars: linguists and

---

*Note: The award-winning manuscript "Sonnets to Human Beings" (Section I of this book) was translated to the German and published in an English/German bilingual edition in October 1992 for the 500th anniversary of the meeting between America and Columbus. *Sonnets To Human Beings / Sonette An Menschen* (Onsabrück, Germany, 1992, ed. Wolfgang Karrer. See Karrer's translation article in Appendix) was so well received by the Germans that it sold out in two years.

literary critics. In addition, because our intent is to present model essays from various perspectives and at different levels so as to inspire students to participate in the dialogues, we include essays by students, as well as faculty of varying ranks.

I have included some interviews with Carmen Tafolla, a prosodic autobiographical sketch, and an essay where Tafolla eloquently advocates teaching composition through creative writing: could our students but be told that they should seek voice in this manner; yes, they would learn the "form" of the language if they were "empowered" and infected with a sense of self and the joy of self expression!

So, to sum up, I suggest that we read this new and challenging poetry while continuously asking ourselves, "'What is it in itself?' Let me ask myself, do 'those' people really speak that way, and might this be a manifestation of the essence of 'those' people? And if I perceive truth of the heart and mind in these poems, then I must further ask if 'those' people are myself. 'What is it in itself?'" Read this mosaic and find the one-to-oneness between art and the culture of a people who stand in the universal place of all mankind.

What spurred me on in this project of putting together a "historical first" — the first critical edition of any work by a Chicano (and, hopefully, there will soon be more to follow) — was the joy and love of Tafolla's poems and stories that my students have expressed over the years.

Ernesto Padilla
Santa Monica, California

. . . because the time has passed when we can afford to write sonnets to just one beloved on a pedestal, the time has come when we must write sonnets to the whole human race, lest before we notice, through our neglect and abuse of *la gente*, we have disappeared entirely from this place,

this book is *dedicado, con respeto,*

to all the human beings who have made my life rich with feelings, ideas, and adventures,

to my *familia,*

y a mi mamá, quien primero me enseñó a amar sin condiciones,

a mi querido sol quien primero me enseñó los sinfines del amor,

a mis hijos,

a mis cielos,

a mis diamantes negros,

y a mi pedacito de turquesa.

Carmen Tafolla
McAllen, Texas

I.
Sonnets To Human Beings

Hot Line

(to my firstborn, firstdead,
para m'ija.)

The mark of you is soft and bright on my body
    The ridge is smooth up my belly
        disruptedly even
        deep and rich in color
                and unforgettable

        like you.

The feel of it against my curious fingers
        is not like skin
        but different
            like promises and memories
            and passionate peace in one.

The scar is somehow like concentrated satin —
        a yard of it per half centimeter —
        rare, distinct, and full of voice and story
            (The aged viejita that I'd met
            so long ago had said
                "Each thing upon this earth
                has voz, virtud, e idioma —
                voice and use and language.")

This mark of you on me
        is full
        of language

    and
    of
    love.

It is your gift to me.
Each night I can reach down and feel it,
listen,
hear your message

on this our own
        private

        red

        hot line.

October 21st, 9 p.m.
(autumn she don't waste no time!)

(to the autumn night sky)

...and the night gets sassy again
and says "no way" she's gonna act hot and white
(or even hi yeller)

when she's *really* feelin' cool and dark and slinky.

No way she's gonna dress up soft, light, sophisticated
and polite

when she's really sharply naked, lustily growin'
at the middle, and with every single
freckle of a star
showin' clear through

(— and no makeup to boot!)

...she gets sassy,
starts breathin' October-like —

shivery and ripe,

late harvest of a lady,
no springtime gentle flower
but one whose womb has swollen
and whose heart has broken
and whose spirit has picked up
and moved on, and grown fuller,
older,
proud.

...the night, she gets sassy,
ready to move up, or move on,
but *move!*— no standin' still
she don't keep life
she swallows it
gustily

drops wiped off with a sleeve
don't wait for table napkins
— they come too late —
Drink life 'n' laugh
'n' let it grow unreined
let it be what it will be
she says

...and her breezes pant strong
she works hard

plays hard
    breathes deep

        blows the useless stuff away —
                like leaves
                    from seasons
                      past
     looks to the root
     goes for the gut

     lays her earthy soul

     right up against her lover-man earth

        with nothin'

          in

        between'm.

Poquito Allá

"This hand?"
"This hand?" he says,
"It was an accident.
You do not understand —
Poquito aquí, poquito allá —
that's how Dios meant it, ves, to be.
It doesn't bother me too much
In fact," he laughs, "It gives me less to work about.
Less people who will trust their broken chairs to me.
Yet I can still these roses plant,
like that one, standing by your feet —
'Las Siete Hermanas,' for they always bloom together,
like sweet sisters — seven in each bunch.
And I can still make *chocolate*, stirring strong,
the fingers do not slow me down —
these two, nor this one, sewed back on.

It's funny, don't you think,
how in those many years at Kelly Field
— or even in the war, Dios solo sabe, so many
around me dead, or legs or arms just floating off to sea —
but I came back (it must have been my mother's prayers)
the only thing the worse for it my teeth
(the Navy took us perfect, sent us back a mess.)
and yet —
I had so much —
aún every limb and digit there.
My whole life full,
and so I can't complain
this hand still does so much
for me — why just today
I planted ten small seeds —
cilantro for Mamá
(that woman loves it even in her beans) —
and pressed the earth down on them soft,
like her soft fingers when she caresses me,
and picked the eggs out for my sisters
y sus nietos — they taste different fresh,
like this — las tiendas no comparan —

But you want to know what happened?
Well, it's not too bad, nomás que
Chuy's neighbor still won't talk to me,

goes way around the grocery store
when he runs into me
I guess he's scared to see.
Los gringos, sometimes, son así.
Se siente mal, because he was the one who said
'Reach down in there for me and get that wrench'
and then he flipped the switch too soon —
ya casi era tiempo de salir —
I'd worked for him all day and he
was eager to pay up, clean up, go home,
and didn't wait to see that it was out.
Así — se acabó.
The doctors sewed this one back on,
aunque los que no están
molestan menos que éste aquí.

Too bad it bothers him so much.
I still do all I used to 'cept for
playing the guitar and carving wood.
The rest I do just fine, tho' maybe not as good.
Y el pobre always was uncomfortable with Mexicans —
Y ahora peor.
Forgot to pay me for that day
or maybe scared to send the cash
for fear I'd ask for more.
Well, that's OK — this hand
still knows to saludar, shake hands, y abrazar
and only yesterday, my baby grandson stood right up,
solito, holding on to these good fingers
here.
Derecho, fuerte, unafraid.
Poquito aquí, poquito allá...."

We Never Die

We never die.
We go through the trees in sunlight
hoping to be seen.
We never die.
We amass ourselves in sand dunes
awaiting patiently
the one who will record
our song.
We never die.
We take the wind's breath
and breathe it slowly
with all the living
with all those who came
before or after us
with all those
who loved
Each in any way
The leaf bending to its branch,
The moon covering her earth asleep
with the warm worn coverlet
of her long black hair,
The unborn child dancing grateful
to the pulse
of its symphony-womb chamber,
And me,
drawn to the light in your eyes
that speaks colors of winter trees,
new-world skies,
dancing pearl-fetus, and sunrise
seen through the eyes
of the sand.

La Miss Low

La Miss Low era alta,
y delgada
y llevaba su pelo
pálido en su cabecita
como la cáscara
de un chícharo . . .
La Rosary siempre quiso peinarla
bien
pa' que se viera
bonita
pero como era maestra,
y nosotros chamacos,
no le dijo
nada.

La Miss Low se paraba
cerquita del Mr. Mason
pensando, creemos,
hacerse más elegante
al pararse cerca
de un hombre,
aún si era casado
y con su crewcut que soló
él pensaba le hacía verse mas galán.
Pero cuando él volteaba
la cabeza
pa' decirle unas palabras,
entre clases, en el corredor ruidoso,
eran nomás ellos,
ellos dos,
héroe y heroína,
entre todos nosotros
chamacos
y se sentía ella
grande
elegante
íntima
riéndose despacio y formal de
cualquiera cosa
con él.

La Miss Low no hablaba mucho
trataba de levantar la cabeza
como figura noble,
de dejar a su silencio
(como guardián de la princesa)

hablar por ella,
cosas complicadas,
y muy sensibles,
de mantener la cara sin expresión,
mostrando así la nobleza de su alma,
de dar un ejemplo altivo
a estos niños incultos.
La Rosary decía que
peinándole el pelo
lleno y suave,
dejándolo crecer
un poquito más,
y poniéndole unos cuantos rizos
Pintándole la cara con más color
y enseñándole a guardar menos
sus emociones,
a mostrar más tranquilamente
su gracia natural,
que la podría
hacer
verse más
bonita.

La Miss Low era alta
y delgada
y posaba
como una estatua
de civilización
sin caos
mientras La Rosary
la veía
como tierra fértil, esperando semillas,
y Rosary allí, queriendo cultivar,
con cariño, su jardín.
"Did you get number 7?" le decía yo,
y abría ella su libro, con un suspiro largo,
diciendo, "Yo la podría hacer
verse muy
bonita."
Pero como era maestra,
y nosotros chamacos,
no le dijo
nada.

Around Us Lie

Around us lie
the messages
babes born voiceless
hearts whose vaults
do not know
how to seal
linked helplessly
to our machines
carrying quiet
the blue eyes that were
requested
while the sun-skinned throngs
fight to eat
and hear no requests
from anyone
The machines laugh smilelessly
they would ask of us
epics
in elaborate colors
but we hum
drumbeats
while carving clean paper
with pens that write
in black ink
only

La Querencia Del Toro

to George and Maria

— *Picked and angered, bleeding from the banderillas wagging on him still
in irritating flashes of sharp ribbon, taunted by the smell and roar of
fear and anxious urging, the bull reaches his querencia, this little holy
high ground he will stand and not leave, until he wins, or dies.*

By four every day the old man is at the park,
limps garbage can to garbage can
takes the empty Coke cans out,
stomps them with his good foot
and stores them in the bag.
The old nun chants "I am not worthy. I am not worthy.
I am not worthy." to her soul,
face blank, from practice.
At four in the morning the middle-aged Chicano
too young, too brown, too smart,
can't sleep from the news, the one
curt page of pretentious evaluation
from a nervous boss whose work he'd done too often,
climbs up Marshall Peak, puffing anger out
and disappointment
meets the tecolote-owl
with wingspan wider than his own
and racing down the hill, survives,
his spirit healed by places
where defeat is honest.

The old white house with gingerbread
trim is torn down by the city
And so the tiny aqua one, built on the half-lot
all the way to the back.
A two-year-old girl, crying angry pride
that Discovery is Punished,
steals the kitchen knife quietly
and builds houses of moist mud
under the house.
These may stay
for quite a while
Until the owl's children
have landed
quietly
on blank-labeled cans.

In Memory of Richi

First day
of school
for both of you
— one of you six and glowing copper,
    running with eagerness and proud
the other 22, young teacher,
    eager for this school

Your blue eyes warm to his brown coals
as you both chat
and share your missions,
as you ask his name.
He rolls it like a round of wealth
and, deep in Spanish tones, responds
    "Richi."
You try to imitate, say
    "Ritchie."
"No!" he teases, confident,
"It's Ri-chi — just like this."
You notice that each syllable
could rhyme with see
and try again.
He pats you on the back.
You go on to your separate tasks —
he to his room, and you to yours.

One day, six hours,
really not a speck of sand
in all this shore of time, and yet,
so crucial,
as you gather papers,
turn to flee the cell
and gain some comfort
in some other place.
Your ray of hope
comes filtering down the hall.
In eagerness for someone's warmth,
you shout and wave,
    "Hey, Richi!"
He corrects,
the light and wealth all gone
from his new eyes,
    "No.
    Ritchie."

In Guatemala

there are no political prisoners
only men's heads that show up sewed
into the now-pregnant bellies
of their fiancé's corpses

only hands that open
from the jungle floor,
fingers crying "¡Justicia!"
as they reach like vines trying
to break free

only butchered organs
pressed into the earth
beneath the feet
of "government" officers

only Ixil Indians in rebellion,
their red woven messages of humanness
in whole Indian villages corraled, beheaded,
for existing too full
of straight-backed dignity

There are no political prisoners
There are no problemas de derechos humanos
There are no repressions in free democracies
There are only Presidents
who scratch each other's backs,
blindfold each other's eyes,
laugh uncomfortably,
puffing the finest
popular-name cigars
and cutting too-human heads
from the non-human bodies
of non-justice.

Sweet Remember

Sweet Remember
when you ask your little girls to be
so sweet,
sit neat,
cry easy,
and be oh so pretty on a shelf

When our young women who are decent
are to always be
in company
of strong young men
who can
protect them

When parents breathe
a sigh of relief
to see their daughters married
and now safe
and someone else's
responsibility

When girls and women
are expected
to play at home, which others should protect,
to always breathe in innocence
and be shielded from heavy news, and death,
to sing and paint
and, when appropriate,
to scream and faint

Sweet Remember
that Marta Diaz de C.
had her legs spread
on an electric bed
as someone probed

with great delight
to see her scream
till dead.

Sweet Remember
that Cristina R.L.G.
was taken in the night
from her parents' home
and husband's bed
and forced to talk with massive rape,
incontinence, indecency,
and forced to faint while hanging by her knees,
wrists tied to feet, till circulation ceased.

Sweet Remember
Elsa B.
whose naked 3-year daughter
was immersed
in ice-cold water,
as the Sergeant pulled her tits and whispered in her ear,
"Whore, come sleep with me
and do it sweetly
or we will not let
the child's head up
until she kicks no more."
And when she did,
they threatened a
Portrait in Two:
Whore and Child Whore —
side by side in bed —
with plenty volunteers
to tear them both
right through the core
mass party rape in
stereo
and screams

galore
"and then we'll know
where we can find
and kill
your husband."
and sad and sick,
to save her child,
she spoke.

And Sweet Remember
young Anita S.
who was raised to think her womanhood
was in her breasts
and inside panties and to be covered
in a dress
and then,
because the village teacher was
a critic
of the government,
and a family friend,
she was "detained,"
and called a Marxist,
had her breasts
slashed at with knives
and bit by soldiers eager
for their flesh
and had then "Communist"
burnt with electric pen
and shocks
into her upper thigh
and her vagina
run by mice,
and lived to know
her womanhood
was in her soul.

and Tina V., María J., Encarnación,
Viola N., Jesusa I., and Asunción
who screamed first and did not think to strike
who'd never fired a gun or learned to fight
who lost their husbands, parents, children, and own lives
and oft'times dignity or body parts or eyes
and some whose pregnant nipples tied with string
were yanked toward opposing walls
and back
till babes were lost
and blood was running black.

Sweet Remember
this is why
I do not ask
my child to cry
to sit sweet helpless and be cute
to always need a male escort
to think that only he protects,
not she, herself, and not she, him
to think herself so delicate
so weak,
to hold as inborn right a man's protection
or his pity for a tear on pretty cheek

But I will teach her
quite instead
that she is her own brave life
till dead
and that there are no guarantees in life
nor rights
but those that we invent
and that the bravest thing of all
to think, to feel, to care, and to recall
is to be human
and to be complete

and face life straight
and stand on solid feet
and feel respect for her own being
temple, soul, and head
and
that she owns her strong brave life
till dead

Porfiria

Porfiria doesn't exist
but if she did
she'd say "¡Que se chingue Reagan!"
      "¡Rómpenles el borlote!"
      y "Tráigame una cerveza, Carlos."

Porfiria liked Carlos –
liked the way he'd take
his pocket knife out,
in front of white liberal gringos
and clean his fingernails with it,
tryin' to look mean,
tryin' to look like the image of Mexicans they were
trying hard to unbelieve.
Porfiria'd say,
not too committed to any one view,
      "Chale, you're okay."

Porfiria didn't like people who were
so committed to the truth
they couldn't see anything else.
But Porfiria wasn't prejudiced —
she didn't like people neither
who were scared of coming down hard
and being violently close-minded —
saying, like those wonderful, crazy intellectuals
visiting from Latinoamérica would say,

¡Está usted loco!
¡Cómo puede creer tal cosa!
¡Está completamente equivocado!
¡Es una tontería increíble!"
She liked that.
Took guts to say it like that,
'steada conference talk, a la USA,
"The distinguished Dr. Satdunk
certainly has a profound comprehension
of the field, but he seems to be forgetting
one major factor, which could disprove
his entire... pardoning my boldness, but..."
Porfiria said that was
      "Chicken shit! Big Mask
      to hide Little Heart!"
or the way she put it
when she was feelin good:

"Paper Prick to hide Bubblegum Huevos."

Porfiria doesn't really exist
but if she did
she'd be the kind to say "Ya Basta,"
put a sig-gar in her mouth,
like Generala Carmen Robles,
1915 Special, Field General, Mexico-style,
with her men and women standing by her,
and say quiet, with the smoke blowin' out slow
every word heavy and dead-eyed
  "Ya ha comenza'o
  la revolución."
and her dead eyes nail you, dying,
with that unspoken final curse word
meanin' "you."

She'd be the kind to get upset about
the uptight, lowdown two-headed academics —
one head playing Brown Beret and
dressing ethnic on the Diez y Seis
(Veevuh luh Rozz-uh, Man!)
other playing bouncing puppy dog
(Yes boss! Yes boss!)
can be bought for less than money —
title, publication,
mention in the Central Office Minutes...
  "Oh, shit!" she'd say,
  then turn and put a crazy GI hat
  on and drink beer to German music
  all night long.

Porfiria'd go home tired
Apologize to her cat
for not putting the food out on time
  Say, "Chinga'as d'esas fregaderas.
  Ni me dejan tiempo de prender la vela."

  "Y ustedes — ¿que?"
responds to puppies scrapping,
nicknamed Gringo and Chicano,
  "A lo menos pueden aprender
  a no cagar en casa ajena."
strokes their necks and
Turns to light the vela
that spiritwarms the house and
catches lightdance off a tear

As "Firia" mends her mother's colcha for her,
thinking.

Porfiria sat on a few committees
was quiet a lot
occasionally mumbled
and once in a while let loose an'
        "¿Y qué pendejos porqué no?"
        or even worse a just plain, "Why?"
Got criticized for "lack of finesse"
and answered, for the soflameros,
        "I handle too much shit
        to use a dust rag and
        furniture polish on it.
        Shovels work just fine."

Porfiria doesn't exist,
in the usual way,
        has no photograph,
        social security number,
        or signature.
But Porfiria has just so damn much to say
that she will show up anyway, stubborn bitch,
that we will
        everyone of us
            take a picture
                invent a number
                    sign a declaration
                            for her
                    even if it has to be
                    with our very own
                        names.

Right in One Language

"Write in one language," they say
and agents sit and glare hairy brows
over foreign words, and almost trying hope,
say, "It's not French, is it?"

But it isn't.

Nor is my mind
when I try tight, clean line
manicured to be like Leave
it to Beaver's house
      straight sidewalk
      so square hedges
      and if there's one on
this   side there's also one on   that
Equally paced
      placed
      spaced
      controlled

"You seem to lose control of the line
in this one," he says, "it all explodes."
    I see bilingüe-beautiful
      explosions —
          two worlds collide
            two tongues dance
              inside the cheek
                together
Por aquí, poquito   and a dash allá también
  salsa — chacha — disco polka
 Rock that Texan cumbia
 in a molcajete mezcla!

But restrain yourself —
the Man pleads sanity —
Trim the excess —
just enough and nothing more
Think Shaker room and lots of light —
two windows, Puritan-clean floor, and chairs
up on clean simple pegs — three —

y
    las
        palabritas
           mías
              are straining at the yoke

two-headed sunflowers
    peeking through St. Moderatius grass
        waiting for familias grandes
garden growing wild
    with Mexican hierbitas, spices, rosas,
      baby trees nurtured así, muy natural
     — no one knows yet
       if they're two years old
       and should be weaned
             or pruned
                or toilet-trained
    but they are given only
    agua y cariñitos,
    shade and sun and compañía
City Inspection Crew,
House and Gardens Crew,
Publications Crew agree
the lack of discipline
lack of Puritan
    purity
      pior y tí.

Chaucer must have felt like this,
   the old Pachuco playing his TexMex onto the page
and even then the critics said,
    "Write
    in one language"
But he looked at all that cleanness, so controlled,
   forms halved, and just could not deny
his own familia, primos from both sides,
            weeds that liked to crawl
            over sidewalks, pa' juntarse,
            visit, stretch out comfy,
            natural and lusty,
            hybrid wealth,
and told them it was just because
he was undisciplined
    unpolished
      and did not know
        how to make love
        with just
        one
        person
        in the room
        or

                    on the page
And he, like me,
did what he wanted anyway
But
You, like they,
want Shaker hallways
and I grow Mexican gardens and backyards.
There are 2 many colors in the marketplace
to play modest, when Mexico and
Gloria Rodríguez say,
"¡Estos gringos con su Match-Match,
y a mí me gusta Mix-Mix!"
There are 2 many cariños to be
                    created
to stay within the lines,
2 many times
when I want to tell you:
                There is room
                    here
                    for two
                    tongues
                    inside this
                    kiss.

Pedacito

When long it takes to craft with care
This miracle of skin and soul and breath,
And blessingworth we find the pain to bear,
Say, "Pedacito de la luna, usted,"
Give light, give love, protect and fuse to heart,
But then the homage pay to death,
See precious life grow tall and march to war,
Immune to wonder then, we halt the breath.

Chest still, moon cold, we distance from the heart.
Forgetting we are linked to light,
The human loses, but we win the war.
What then the goal? Why cannot we respect
To see in life's form fully grown,
Say, "Pedacito de mi corazón?"

Beyond Our Own

Heeding the call of a mockingbird
whose voice has crackled with the plight
of unknown days and loveless nights
and human voices left unlearned,
it is but time that we have left
to bargain with in measured bits
and say to him, "We know the plea,
but have no answer ready yet,
no face with which to give us sight,
no heart of which to give our face."
We are inferior to your heed,
for we have yet to hear the voices —
even one beyond our own.
Not even one beyond our own.

The Magic

to the child in the photo (and all the others)

Such magic in a child there is, such life,
Such fountainburst of days of love and hope,
The magic breath of tiny hands and heart
That beat and breathe and suffer try, and cope.
But ribs, like tree roots arching to the skies,
Face upward, caking o'er the ground so dry,
And hunger curls the spine, affronts our eyes:
You will not live. And yet, you will not die.

The love that ripened in your first wet cry,
The hope that sheltered you when arms could not
Will not retreat nor silent keep their sigh:
In naked truth they lash our superficial lies
    (like war and wealth and coldness comfort-taught.)
Your eyes now frozen in the lens and paper flat
    give hope that our hearts cold might yet survive.
For this, you will not know but grace, and, dove,
In truth as death, you will not be but love.

Living on the San Andreas

Wondering if Nostradamus meant us...
Wondering if the California Indians' claim
the air made us crazy was...
Wondering if the smog has done that already
Wondering why there are so few poets
in this town
or if blindness will bring sanity
wondering why I pull my hair out
by the roots
criticizing the ends
Wondering why we are straddling this
daily,
babes in our arms,
Wondering what
we are doing
here.

Statue Of

Statue of
Teeming hordes of hungry
Always wanting just a
Time of rest not waiting
Under suffocated souls
Even scared to breathe too loud

Or ask
Freedom from the

MIGRA who will hunt them down

The Urge to Write

The urge to write
to squeeze your child until she breathes
The urge to write
to take the cut head down from the tree

The urge to rain dance, rain dance
pour the teardrops on the tongues
cool the fevers
hock for grain the guns
Pour the sweat from spas
onto the dying fields
Take the steam from worry greed
into village kitchens, warm the frozen bodies
give them meals

Sundance kiss the stiffened lids of corpses
open eyes from death and hate
pump the hearts with open palms
bow to nature breath and reins

The urge to sieve the rivers
                red with blood
return the hearts to lovers praying
To rebuild, clay by clay, with sun,
with water, food, and touch, the human form
To peel off finecloth uniforms
and turn them to the bandage
To touch the skin until it shivers warm

The urge to take the huddled bodies
out of tunnels, trunks — Beknight
with life and freedom
and with right

The urge to
Breathe

The urge to shout
Do not die
   alone

Concha's Brother

Concha's brother
beat his first wife
(and said he loved her still today)
always got drunk for funerals
and tried to ready-start a fight
with any gringo, especially a cop,
sometimes cheated people who came to his garage
always got angry at anyone waiting on him
and liked to say, "Where there's smoke, there's fire."

Concha's brother
wrote all the bad checks,
got all the girls pregnant,
crossed all the lights late,
and even stole a fifty dollar book for me once,
and gave it to me, *con mucho respeto.*

Concha's brother
made the best *fajitas,*
barbecued like a reigning king,
and did it in the front yard, inviting everyone,
especially on special occasions,
like the birthday of his daughter,
(daggerdeep dimples like he,
and laughing)
telling jokes like only he could,
adding extra spice to everything
and everyone drinking
all they could.

Concha's brother
divorced his second wife,
remembered neat times with the first,
said again he loved her still
and always played pool with
her brothers.

Concha's brother
cried late at night
all alone
and the tears mixed
with the beer
and the sweat
and the loneliness,

and the only things
that brought
the sun
up
for another day
were his daughter,
the jokes he told so good,
and those barbecued *fajitas*
he did in the front yard
inviting
everyone

Chispa, The Pachuco Sonnet

When stubborn Chispa takes cowhead and tripe,
And makes of it a feast that thirty years
Will turn into expensive fare and ripe
To whims elite from poverty's arrears,
And ese vato glides, his pose the deer's,
But head held back at angle to the sun,
The slant of pyramids his body hears.
The Aztec thus danced too, same angle done.
Another's gesture comes from Babylon.
The word from Africa transforms, survives.
The song of China lingers on the tongue.
Posed also to the sun, Quetzalcoatl smiles.
Chispaseed, the spirit never dies, the flame
of centuries' sabor is carried on, the same.

Come With Me People

Come with me people
Let me feel the soft breeze
smiling closed eyes
with cuddled love.

Come with me people
Let me feel your blood slow
with the morning sun
and your heart beat plain
like the country axe at its daily wood.

Come with me people
Let me feel your breath drawn in
deep and long and drinking full
the scent and feel and warmth
of human breath around you,
used and re-used like a kitchen tool
passed from one to next to next,
gaining flavor and smooth edges.

Come with me people
Come with me now
and let us leave behind
those tiny orbs of shining steel
where people keep themselves
so safe
so separate
and
so all alone.

Come with me people
Let me come with you
to where air and sun and living spirits
blend together
gently.

To where air
and sun
and living spirits
blend
together
gently.

Nine Moons Dark

— This is what it takes to make a child —

Nine new moons of dark hot wind
and careful mouthfuls, hoarded, pointed,
sent direct to fill the small one,
Empty *jarros*, *ollas*, make the magic prayer,
and corn tortillas carry forth alone
the gifts of all.

Grace from spiritdancers gives the balance
over holes and rocks
that make the street,
to keep the swollen womb
from falls and blows.

One treasure-bought
small handmade *vela*,
lit in prayers to
Indian Pregnant Virgin,
still in name the goddess free
pre-fires and pre-cross
Guadalupe
Tonantzín.

And last a blessing
from the eldest face of corn
Hand, even warmer, gives the
touch, the shape
of welcome.

    Past the rabid dogs
    the knifecold brows
    the hungry pouts
    searching for purse —
    there is none.
    Past the street lights' angry metal blare.
    Past the profit eyes
    that buy the babes
    before their birth,
    Grabbing,
    appetize a bill for 50, 20, any
    strange-faced tender
    under trembling fingers
    of the ones whose other
    children starve at home

and some, caught between
foodsilence and
fullarmscrying,
follow, into
a car.

Past the doors of public *Hospital Civil*,
pulling her *rebozo* tighter
round her dropping belly, rising life,
her tiny claim intact.
Nineteen years seems
long enough to wait
for this small cry,
the very first,
Feels the head emerging
strong

the tiny heart pounds out
its shout of proud Survival

small investment, kicking
whisked away
passed hand to hand
change arms to arms to beds
and on the road, new papers, forms
a neat 10,000 chopped
in many stops and stages
To Northern Nursery's Lie:
Money buys it
all.

And somewhere at the *Hospital Civil*,
A scream undying burns:
This one's not mine!
This dead one pulled from your *hielera*
for the cool fleshmarket's use
The scream goes on, unchanging, strong,
as if to heat their hells
and rip their walls
and reach the wind, to touch
that one of hers,
so far.

Nine new moons of Indian-color-earth enfolding
warm as blood and turquoise-feathered prayers
and all they give her
is that purpled baby, cold

from the refrigerator,
thrice-abandoned one, reused
to move their market

that baby
cold
touched soft at last
by her painpartner fingers
whom even her
long burning scream
of rage and love
cannot
warm.

marked

Never write with pencil,
m'ija.
It is for those
who would
erase.
Make your mark proud
    and open,
Brave,
       beauty folded into
  its imperfection,
Like a piece of turquoise
    marked.

Never write
with pencil,
m'ija.
Write with ink
  or mud,
or berries grown in
gardens never owned,
    or, sometimes,
     if necessary,
      blood.

They Come From Within Us

They come from within us
those unwhispered spiritchildren of our souls,
from within the fifth womb of us
unbirthed spiritchildren,
conceived and then dissolved,
absorbed into us

You will see them
everytime I dance forgotten swirls
You will hear them
in the quiet eeking half-screams
    in the night
You will know them
in those strange glances
that lightning from my eyes
    but do not
    belong to me

They come from within us
spiritchildren that
bloomed in
tiny half-buds
deep in our untainted hideaways
in the fifth womb
of the fifth soul
where their spirits rested
long enough
to give their presence
to us
and then disappear,
goodby-whisper unannounced,
blend into our blood,
kiss the holy quiet spots
and leave,

the spirit tracks still in us

They come from within us
When you hear me
instead of them
it is by chance
for they come soft and silent,
resting only
between
missions
and
within us.

Mission San José

The rocks are warm
have had the hands upon them
through the years
with sun to bake in
memories.
Gentle, even with
ungentle missions,
somehow life got through
to Them,
the priests amazed
that rabbit tasted
good,
slowed their passion fervor
one San Antonio sunny afternoon
learned to
lope
a bit
and breathe
with warm brown human flesh
touched the rocks in
tenderness
one time too many,
ceased to call it mission
as it grew to make itself
home
for all of us.

hay un lugar

Hay un lugar
There is a place
where corn is ground by daily arms
and old metate smoothed by flow of family
to make tamales where the kernels
keep their character
and wealth

There is a place
where supper tables feel the pulse of human hands
and breathe it back to them, with blessings,
respecting life and death and age, each in the other,
thing of flesh to thing of wood,
with boundaries forgotten

There is a place
where the stone comal warms gifts
from gardens that are asked,
and each plate is prepared
and carved to fit the tastes
for that one mouth
whose sounds are known so well
and warmth is added from the hands that love

There is a place
where early morn adobe walls
retain the day's high sun
and spread its warmth so kindly
through the night

There is a place where hands grow old,
the wrinkles kept intact and kissed,
a place where babies still get bounced
to dancing-song of whisper:
"all the world's your own"
where eyes lift up in gratitude to sky, and
even zopilotes have a softness to their name

There is a place
hay un lugar
donde hay un lugar para tí

Ancient Workers

the hand

shows lines

engraved

by ancient workers

each in line

chipped out its mark

to write the letter

say

we are all here

together

in you

Gift Design

made for an older human

Turquoise speaks the fire

 and the soul.

White shells, the Peace.

Brown twigs,

children of the branches,

the evidence of imperfection,

highest compliment.

Vision of a Former Life

Breathe
shallow
Breathe
like sand in sunlight
poised silent

A dog crosses
the Pueblo afternoon,
absorbs the shadows

To arrange
the painting in the sand
(my work)
    I do not place
    the pieces
    I breathe
    with them,
    lightly

No Tienes Límites

a slice of you
does not fit on paper

        (unless one wears
        glasses ground with filters
        for the sun)

a slice of you
bursts with pleasure
in the mouth
can only be tasted
at midnight
when ink cannot testify
and time and consciousness
are turned off
so humans can exist
without limitations

In Love With People

It occurs to me that we
are all in love with people.
We see the plump-pout lower lip,
the smoothness of a temple scar,
the eye that flickers between words
and, on them, shrouds in cinders.
We lie in wait to see them pass
and drink up, as they talk.
I stare at this one with wide hips
and full moon eyes — the weight looks good
it settles soft, relaxed, no laws,
And that one there, my *primo*,
just a little bit *loquito*,
eyes a little crossed, wire glasses little
out-of-style, smile a little sweet,
frame a little tall and bent.
The ten-year-old *pachuco*-child
trying so hard to be so cool,
shows me the way to "pop,"
the way to "break," then shyly states,
"I do it better than this
sometimes."
It occurs to me that we
are all in love with people.
The way the strands soft-frame the face
or teeth jut out so brave and out of place
but innocent; on this one here the nose
turns pointed down, suspiciously;
on this one apple cheek crowds cozy
up against white lashes cuddling.
The way that wee hand clings,
its dimples hugging wrinkles;
that smile so full of metal teeth;
that face so dark that it absorbs;

the way the thousand craters on this face
are like a lava field, complex and rare,
or other things that catch us
loving people — how your eyes
stop like culprits caught when asked
to think what you want, not what I,
How Lopez limps up slow and shy
to say hello — how Pino never hesitates,
How this one here laughs quietly, abrazos out,
and that one cries at night
and we all hurt one time or more
and long to feel that drumming heart nearby.
The specks of dust quickscatter, die,
each one seen only once, and through a different sky.
It does occur to me that we
are all in love with people.

How Shall I Tell You?

*after listening to the world news, the U.S. attack
on Libya, the Soviet accident at Chernobyl, the
firing in the Persian Gulf, and wondering...if...*

When no soul walks the softened green
and no foot beats the pulse on crumbling brown
and no one lives to sing to rain
or soak to sun the spirit of its golden gown
to weave the many colors of the after-arch
from sky to human skin to wooded wealth
in fiber fabrics beads and tusks and seeds
all leading up in rows of beauty drumbeat to black
    neck, like venison in stealth

When no one lulls the child to sleep
or takes the wrinkled story's hand
or listens to the news — a wired sound
of tribe on tribe and — stet now — man on man
how shall I tell you that I love you then?
How shall I touch your fingers tip to tip
    and say that we were blood and human voice and friend?

II.
Selected Poems

Mi Tía Sofía

Mi Tía Sofía
sang the blues
at "A" Record Shop
on the west side of downtown,
across from Solo-Serve's
Thursday coupon specials
she never missed
    — "Cuatro yardas de floral print cottons por solo eighty-nine cents —
    fíjate nomàs, Sara, you'll never get it at that price anywhere else!"
    she says to her younger sister.
And "A" Record Shop
grows up the walls around her like vines
like the flowers and weeds and everything in her
green-thumb garden
But here —
instead of cilantro and rosas
and Príncipe Dormido —
it's a hundred odd and only 45's
10 years too late
that'll never be sold
even after she dies
and a dozen hit albums that crawl up the wall,
smiling cool pachuco-young Sonny and the Sunglo's,
The Latin Breed, Flaco Jimenez, Toby Torres,
and the Royal Jesters.
Also: Little Stevie Wonder.
And The Supremes.
She sings to pass the time
"Ah foun' mah three-uhl
own Blueberry Hee-uhl."
She also likes "Lavender Blue."
It seems to be her color,
but *bright* — in a big-flowered cotton print
(from Solo-Serve.)

Tía Sofía speaks Tex-Mex
with Black English
and *all* the latest slang.
Not like the other aunts —
Tía Ester, always at home,
       haciendo caldo,
       haciendo guiso,
       haciendo tortillas,

she never left the house
except to go to church,
braided her hair on top of her head
and always said,
"Todos los gringos se parecen."
(All Anglos look alike.)
or Tía Anita — always teaching,
    smart, proper, decent,
Tía Sara, Tía Eloisa, Tía Febe —
all in church, always in church.
Sofía said, "Well, I play
Tennessee Ernie Ford and Mahalia Jackson
on Sunday mornings."
And she *did*,
and sang along,
never learning that only singing in church
"counted."
    She never made it through school either.
    Instead of ethnic jokes,
    the family told Sofía jokes:
    "Remember that time at the lake, con Sofía?
    — Sophie! Come out of the water! It's raining!
    — No, me mojo! (I'll get wet!)
    They were always a little embarrassed by her
        lack of wisdom,
        lack of piety.

After she died, they didn't know what to say.
Didn't feel quite right saying
"She's always been a good Christian."
So they praised the way
"siempre se arreglaba la cara,"
"se cuidaba,"
and the way she never "fooled around"
even though she could've
after Uncle Raymond died,
When she was still young.
(Only 71).

Funeral comes every 2 years in the family now
— just like the births did
60 to 80 years ago.
I remember a picture of a young flapper
with large eyes — Tía Sofía.
Between the tears
we bump into the coffin by accident,

and get scared
and start laughing.
It seems appropriate.
I also feel like singing
in a Black Tex-Mex
"Blueberry Hee-uhl."

Allí por la Calle San Luis

West Side — corn tortillas for a penny each
    Made by an aged woman
      and her mother.
    Cooked on the homeblack of a flat stove,
    Flipped to slap the birth awake,
    Wrapped by corn hands.
Toasted morning light and dancing history —
    earth gives birth to corn gives birth to man
    gives birth to earth.
Corn tortillas — penny each.
    No tax.

At the Very Last Battle

The wooden rocking-horse in Reyes Cardenas' yard
Sinks on bended knee like Chief Joseph
at the very last battle.

Staring into the ground and biting on its bit,
Saying, "I am tired. My heart is sad and sick.
I will fight no more."

The only Mexican-American principal in Seguin
Waves a sad beer bottle at my Pacer
as it passes.

I drive up to my assigned parking space
And wonder if my lot is taken by the car next door
or if I really belong.

I turn the key and walk into the empty house,
Alone, like the rest of la raza,
a stranger in my own home.

Como Un Pajarito

Mi tía tenía 71 años
Con trenzitas blancas, hechas de historia y de inocencia,
Trenzitas hechas a mano, hechas por su madre cada mañanita
    a las seis de la mañana cuando la casa está
    fría y sólo los pájaros se levantan.
Mi tía tenía 71 años y trenzitas blancas.

Sus ojos cocinaban pan dulce y daban de comer a los niños.
Todos eran sobrinos. Todos eran mi'jito.
Chanclas en ritmo paciente venían a ayudar.
Una sonrisa de Pascuas y del almuerzo,
Dos hoyuelos llenos de susto, risa, y cinco años de edad,
Manitos de masa de tortillas.
Mi tía tenía 71 años y una vida de despertar a sus 6 de
    la mañana, sus 6 apreciada.

      — Su carne, helada,
    Sus huesos pediches,
    la boca chueca, seca — dos dientes de piedra vieja.
    En cama desesperada hecha de trabajo y medicina
    agria...quejitas y suspiros —
    "¿Dónde estoy?"
    ...quejitas y suspiros,
    Un perro asoleado y loco...
    Hambre pesado en la cabeza...
    Desconocido sentado en la veranda...
    Sangre en la rodilla — "te caístes de la bicicleta.
      A la otra no te vayas tan lejos de la casa,
      ¿eh?"...
    Pan bien quemado — que lástima...
    Tanto trabajo todavía y ya son las ocho de la noche...
    Ya hize avena y no hay azúcar...
    Me perdí en el centro. Ni pude hallar la calle
      Comercio...
    El dentista te va sacar todo, todo...
    Gato roñoso, se le está cayendo la oreja...
    Hace mucho calor, y esta lana picosa, esta cama y
      esta lana picosa...
    Casa vacía — todos están de vacación
        Menos yo.

Tía, ¿dondé estás?
...El invierno en las venas.
    Chanclas calladas —
      Pájaro sin canción.

Mi tía tenía 71 años.
Una quejita muy chiquita
    y se murió.
Una quejita de pájaro
    y cerró sus alitas.

Los Corts (5 voices)

Los Corts 1. (la madre)

Las dos de la tarde y el calor.
Sudor pegajoso saliendo hasta de los ojos.
Cuando yo era chamacuela, me encantaban estas tardes,
Porque podía ir a buscar los gatos del barrio dormiditos
    en sus rincones
Pero ahora es m'ija la que les va a buscar,
Sí, esos mismos gatos roñosos y flacos.
Y yo que ya no puedo respirar de tanto calor que hace
    en este cuartito.
Me acuerdo de cuando era muy bonita —
Ahora el cuerpo se me va desbaratando cada día
Y la cara se va cayendo, y cuando lo arreglo
Parece de plástico, o de payasa.
¿Ya qué soy? Sólo sudor y dolores.
Uju — el bebito ya se despertó.
Mañana tendré que ir a welfare.
…Las tres de la tarde y el calor.

Los Corts 2. (el chamaquito)

¡Jiiiii-jo! ¡Me jayé un daime!
¡Ta hueno eso!
Pa los airplanes que venden de wood
(¿O eran de cuara esas?)
Nuimporta — hasta los beisbol carts se compran a nicle,
(También esos dientes de wax…)
Cuando llega Deri del trabajo, le voy decir,
O le asusto con los dientes.
Y esa vieja mala de la tiendita
que siempre me 'tá regañando,
Le voy *enseñar* ese daime
Pa que *vea*
Pa que *vea*…

Los Corts 3. (la pachuquita)

Oye tú — nomás no. La Silvia no vale nada.
Ta bien puta. Corriendo tras el Larry. Y él no la quiere.
Yo sé — porque me anda buscando a mí. He tol' my brother.
Y después he asked me if I'd meet him a la tiendita after school.
'Ta bien cool ese — ta pero *chulo*. Es
el más good-looking de to'a la class. Jijo, y el otro día,
traiba esa camisa azulita, con el collar p'arriba así,
y se veía su medallón en el chest,
y como siempre los zapatos shainados y el white hanky —
¡'ta bien pacito!

Y La Silvia piensa que lo va agarrar
— pero nomás con cadenas, muchacha —
porque anda trás ésta aquí. Y yo no lo voy correr.
Me dicen que she's gonna jump me,
pero tú no te apures, 'manita — yo me defiendo
Pinche puta, con la navaja se la entierro esas ideas. Yo me
defiendo. Porque nadie le insulta a La Dot.

...Ey — la Mary Pester le 'taba escribiendo
dirty notes a La Silvia, y ella tambíen patrás —
y 'taban diciendo malas cosas de Teodora. Me dijo Rosie.
Y que Manda y Rosie y la Teodora s'iban a juntar en P.E.
para dárselo a Pester y a Silvia...
— You *bet* muchacha! Aquí 'toy — lista!
Ajá, y a ver a quién más juntamos, porque La Silvia
se junta con todas esas gordonas feotas
que 'tan pero perras pa' pelear.
Si, en las showers,
pa' que no vea la Miss Hensley
porque no le gusta que peleamos
en el gym floor.

Los Corts 4. (the dropout)

N'ombre, ya no voy.
Aunque 'buelita me diga.
Ese honroom teesher joto, pinche, caga'o
Ya no pue'e 'cerme na'a.
¡Porque yo no me dejo!
¿Y qué se creen?
Tan fufurrí y tan smart que se creen —
yo *no soy* tonto.
Pero me ponen las *hardest* questions —
Yo no soy tonto.
¿Y qué m'importa?
¿Y qué m'importa si soy tonto?
¡Mejor que ser joto!
They don' *like* me, y siempre acusándome a mí.
N'ombre, ya no voy.
Aunque 'buelita me diga.
(And I *wasn't* spikking Spenish.
I *wasn't!!*)

Los Corts 5. (la viejita)

Sí, entre, entre.
Usted es la que trabaja con El Padre Rodríguez. Pos la cosa es humilde, pero
es suya. Para servirle, Teófila Hernández de Soto.
Soto, ese fue mi esposo. Sí, el de ese retrato allá —
Cuando éramos jovencitos — reciéncasaditos — nomás
teníamos el Benny Chuniar y La Lupita. Uh — y la Lupita ya
es grande — ya hasta se casó su *hijo*. Ese es, sí, ese en el T.V. —
cuando fue su gradu-ey-chon de jaiskul. Y esa bebita ahí en la
mesita es mi nieta, la más reciente, pero allí nomás tenía los tres
años, y ahora fíjate que ya tiene los siete.
Sí, tengo muncha familia — digo, de los hijos y los nietos —
porque ya de primos y de hermanos ya casi todos se han
muerto. De hijos y de hijas tengo munchos, y nunca me dejan
sola. Todos se han casado menos m'ijo el menor, Rudy
(Rudolfo le puse, como mi hermano). Ese es, el que
está de uniforme de solda'o. Sí, fue para Vietnam y gracias
a Dios, me lo mandaron bueno y sano otra vez. Nomás que
me lo llevaron de muy muchacho y muy simpático y siempre
sonriendo, y ahora a veces se me pone medio-triste y se mete
a pelear. Me dice que es porque le hacen menos y le insultan.
Y dice que a veces es porque es mexicano. Y yo le digo que
más antes, fue peor, y que su papá también tuvo que
defenderse, ha sido así por mucho tiempo, que no se enoje.
Pero no puede hallar trabajo,
y, a veces, yo entiendo
y yo también me enojo,
pero nomás aquí adentro.
Aquí
adentrito,
y no le digo a nadien.

Salvation, In Poor Clothing

I remember
our "tough" neighborhood,
junior high,
early 60's,
boys who'd take the white hanky
to the nose
and presume to sniff some
status,
bragging themselves big,
while others of us knew
there wasn't anything but
old cotton fabric and soap
they were smelling.

"Mentiras!" we would toss away
their shocking gesture,
disbelieving.

We knew
none of us had enough
money
to buy glue.

Los Loquitos

Sépase que
    en el barrio mexicano
siempre hay
                    los loquitos

Entiende que
    no just *hay*
pero hay
    in a special way

Véase que forman
    parte
and people see them
    y los saludan
y, casi con respeto
    se dice —
        A'í viene el loquito
y simplemente, people just
    los acomodan
            ¿sabes?

Y de vez en cuando
    viene la loquita
        a sentarse en tu veranda
        pareciendo tener un
        argumento fuerte con
                    alguien

y de vez en cuando
    viene el loquito
        y te dice
        que todos los perros
        están rabiosos
        y que te debes
                    cuidar

y de vez en cuando...
    se muere un loquito
y todos dicen
    "Pobrecito"
y en poco tiempo aparece
                    otro

y de vez en cuando viene
    a decirte que el cielo
        se está acercando demasiado

         y que te debes
                    cuidar
y la vida sigue,
        entre perros, locos, y verandas
y las casas se pintan
ésta azul, ésa café
        y ésa
                    color de rosa
Sépase que
        en el barrio mexicano
siempre hay
                los loquitos

Aquí

He wanders through the crooked streets
   that mimic river beds Before,
   and breathes the anxious air in traffic
   filled with tension left from wooded crossroads in attack.
   He shops the windows, happy,
   where the stalking once was good
   and his kitchen floor is built on bones
   of venison once gently roasted.

"It's a good place for a party!" he concurs
to friends now dressed in jeans.

     The ground was already beaten smooth
     and festive by the joy of ancient dances.

He feels the warmth,
and doesn't know his soul is filled
with the spirit of coyotes past.

Memories

Medina Magiadora
  My campmeeting-preacher grandfather
   used to wash souls here
    baptizing them
    in the name of.

  My fronteriza-fuerte great-grandmother
   washed clothes here
    scaring the stains away
    from her loved ones' clothes.

I only wash memories
  of lives and times I never knew
  Dipping them delicately
  in the soft waters of the shady
  Medina
  softly polishing them clean
  until the faces of the past are clear
    ...hello, great-grandma,
    in your 1867 norteña vaquero jacket
    and your tiny unconquerable
    face and frame.
    ...the frozen crisp image of a little boy
    guiding log-laden mules
    through the icy mountain morning,
    dreaming of running far away
    from his dead parents' graves,
    dreaming of being far away
    from the cold and the death...
    . . . a bugler in the Civil War
    who didn't speak English.
    . . . Indian chicken-thief taking
    out his anger on the small farms
    around San Antonio,
    taking his tiny brigade
    on a joy-ride chicken-shout celebration
    bareback around their civilization
    taking what was his.
    . . . A worried family offering a white horse instead
    so Pancho Villa wouldn't take their youngest son
    as soldier.
    ...A widow crossing an unimportant river,
    later to become the Greenback-Wetback Curtain...
    ...A Basque street urchin flippantly jumping aboard-

ship for an unknown world
easy to conquer
in his young
pickpocket mind.
...una india, maidservant in the colonizer's house,
desired and daring, too efficient, too beautiful, too smart,
chased out after she bore his child,
alone but strong,
still studying, still too smart.
...quiet centuries of sailors and seashore dreamers,
quiet farmers, loud gypsies, songmakers and metalworkers,
maids, cooks, tutor-nursemaids, blacksmiths and woodcarvers
flow here from the ocean.
...star-scholars, hunters, potters, dreamworkers,
curanderas, earthworkers, drum-dancers,
sun-worshippers and river-followers
pour here from the land.
...vaqueros, fronterizos, rebeldes and
as always, dreamers, poets
grow here,
breathe here now,
drinking from the waters
of the Medina,
Medina Magiadora.
Aquí estoy,
lavando mi herencia.
Here I am
washing
my heritage.

Voyage

I was the fourth ship
    Behind Niña, Pinta, Santa María,
    Lost at sea while watching a seagull,
    Following the wind and sunset skies,
    While the others set their charts.

I was the fourth ship,
    Breathing in salt and flying with clouds,
    Sailing moonbreezes and starvision nights,
    Rolling into the wave and savoring its lull,
    While the others pointed their prows.

I was the fourth ship.
    Playfully in love with the sea,
    Eternally entwined with the sky,
    Forever vowed to my voyage,
    While the others shouted "Land."

La Malinche

Yo soy la Malinche

My people called me Malintzín Tepenal
The Spaniards called me Doña Marina

I came to be known as Malinche
    and Malinche came to mean traitor.

They called me — *chingada*
                    ¡Chingada!

(Ha — ¡Chingada! Screwed!)

Of noble ancestry, for whatever that means, I was sold into slavery
by MY ROYAL FAMILY — so that my brother could get my
                                                inheritance.

...And then the omens began — a god, a new civilization,
                                the downfall of our empire.

    And *you* came.
        My dear Hernán Cortés, to share your "civilization" —
                                            to play a god,

    ...and I began to *dream*...
            I *saw*,
                    and I *acted*!

I saw our world
    And I saw yours
        And I saw —
                another.

And *yes* — I helped you —
                (against Emperor Moctezuma Xocoyotzín himself!)

I became Interpreter, Advisor, and lover.
    They could not imagine me dealing on a level with you —
        so they said I was raped, used,
                    chingada
                        ¡Chingada!

But I saw our world
    and your world
        and another.

No one else could *see*!
        Beyond one world, none existed.
        And you yourself cried the night
        the city burned,

and burned at your orders.
The most beautiful city on earth
                in flames.
You cried broken tears the night you saw your destruction.
My homeland ached within me
                (but I saw *another*!)

Another world —
        a world yet to be born.
And our child was born...
        and I was immortalized ¡*Chingada!*

Years later, you took away my child
(my sweet mestizo new world child)
        to raise him in your world.
        You still didn't see
                You *still* didn't see.
And history would call *me*
                        chingada.

But Chingada I was not.
    Not tricked, not screwed, not traitor.
For I was not traitor to myself —
        I saw a dream
            and I reached it.
                Another world...

                        La raza.

                    la raaaaaaaa-zaaaaa...

Si escuchas el viento . . .

Si eschuchas el viento nocturno.
Que en respiros profundos te sopla
— es que te lleva el mensaje
   de mi amor eterno para tí.

Si ves la luna gentil
Que acaricia su cielo moreno
— es que te susurra el poema
   de mi amor eterno para tí.

Si sientes las estrellas festivas
Que explotan en alegría
— es que te cantan la melodía
   de mi amor eterno para tí.

Y si te toca el calor de la noche,
O la frescura de la brisa,
O lo oscuro de las sombras,
O la luz de una sonrisa,
— Sepa que sólo sun mensajeros
   De mi amor eterno para tí.

Loca

Loca
  loca soy
    loca melena deritiendo palabras y brisas
    lavándolas en el río.

    gitana coja soplando tempestad loca
    y chupándose los dedos después de sus mangos.

    gritana tuerta cantado a la luna loca
    y echándose unas polkitas
    con cualquierquestáenpantalones.

      Loca, loca, de fantasma boca
      que te escapan tus ojos
      y te vuela tu troca.

loca,
    loca cuna con motor y orquesta
    llantas nuevecitas, la garantía sirve por un año.

    loca colima pintándose la cara con zoquete
    y ponte tu ombligo en el hoyuelo.

    loca rodilla que se sangra y se dobla
    y se cae sin amigos mientras te mueres de risa.

      Loca, loca, de vestido de fríjol
      arroz en el molcajete
      y blanquillos de mármol.

Loca,
  loca soy
    loca vela loca, prendida entra glaciares,
    bañándose cada sábado con jabón de casa
                en una lágrima.

Tierra Brujo

perceptions
    spiraled lizards
        del desierto wilderness
        de mi *terra incognita*,
      wild country
          avoided by the civilized,
          feared-worshipped by adventurers.

    ojos de iguana
    esqueleto de arco iris
    noche prowling through aullido's echo
      into the sun-brittled day,
        daring the undaunted
        dissecting the insincere.

Tierra Brujo,
    cactus cuna,
    defying comfort
    you break your milkteeth on montañas
    and nurse yourself on sudor.

Tierra Brujo
    por más que han tratado
    nunca te han conquistado.

Curandera

Afuera de tu casa,
   entre la hierba buena y el aníz
   estoy planteada.

Vine aquí a verte,
  a preguntar tus ojos tierra-grises
   a escuchar tu voz mesquite seco
    a observar tus manos sabi-siglos
     a llevarme alguna hierba de una de tus botellas.

      The smell of her kitchen and the sound
        of her chanclas
      are almost within my sight. Her wisdom,
      the secrets that age has let grow
      slowly
      in her window
      like a wild coffee-can-seeded plant of
        no name
      of no dignity or fuss
      beyond that
      of its own
      presence.

      Those aged clouded eyes have seen the
        bodies of the dead
      sink below the crust of red-dirt sand
      and felt the swelling stomach's gift
      emerge a blood-red man.
      Observing, sinking in thoughts,
      I have gone no further.
      At a distance that will not stand still.
      My feet stuck, rooting

  The gnarled and earthing fingers of her mind
    feel the current in my veins
      and see the twilit shapes within my bodycaverns

Curandera,
   te siento arrastrando tus chanclas por los arcos-portales
    de mis venas,
   bajando los botes de tu sabiduría del gabinete
    de mi cabeza

El perro aulla, el rocío me resfría,
mis pies cementados en sus huellas,
mis ojos mudos preguntando a la luz de tu ventana.
Tiemblo aquí en tu jardín,
entre la hierba buena y el aníz.

— El horno es terremoto dormido...

En tus ollitas hierben ya

las hojas

de mis sueños.

woman-hole

Some say there is a
vacuum — a black hole —
    in the center of womanhood
      that swallows countless
        secrets and has strange
          powers

Yo no sé desas cosas
solo sé que the
    black echo is music
      is sister of sunlight
        and from it
          crece
            vida.

La Isabela de Guadalupe y El Apache Mío Cid

I, as an India,
And you, as a Spaniard,
    How can we ever make love?

I, by mecate tied
    to a red dirt floor
    y una casucha de adobe
    en las montañas de cool morning
    and the damp of the wet swept floor.

Y tú, with your fine-worked chains
    Tied from armor to iron post.
    White stallions and engraved gateways
    And a castle of hot night,
    Fine tablecloth, and chandelier etiquette.
    And pierce-eyed thoughts
    From the noble-blooded soul.
    Rey en España,
    Hacendado en México,
    Y Emplumado Emperador entre los Aztecas.

    Pero yo NUNCA FUI dese tipo!
    En España, gitana
    En México, criada
    Y hasta entre Aztecas,
    yo no fui Azteca, sino obrera,
    cara triste,
    y calma.

I, que me gusta andar descalsa,
y tú, bordado en hilos de oro,
    How can we ever make love?

Will I have to crawl inside your armor?
Will you have to paint your feet with dirt?
Will we have to stop the world, take off its reins,
    and tell it to go ver si puso la marrana?

Have you ever seen mecate elope with chains?

Will we have to meet between the day and night,
enlazados, escondidos, entejidos en amor,
with two masks and jet-way tickets labeled "Smith"?

Will we make a funny pair —
    red dirt floor and chandeliers?

(Did we make that house already?)

Did we already shift the worlds,
blend over blend in prism states,
moving between the mirrors of our many, many lives?

Dime, ¿am I really the criolla en manta?
        ¿Are you really the apache in armor?
        Who did this for us already?
        Who gave my life to you to me to
        you and made it many-colored one?

I, as an India,
And you, as a Spaniard,
        How can we ever make love?
I as an India and?
— You as campesino and?
— I as la reina and?
— You as indito and?
— Yo la azteca and?
— Tú el tolteca and?
— Yo la poblana y?
— Tú Mío Cid y?
— Yo la mora y?
— Tú el judío y?
— Nosotros la gente y
            nosotros
                la gente
                    y....
                        Amamos.

Ancient House

In that tall-ceilinged ancient eight-walled house
 where all my midnight dreams are born
  cuddled like children, fed chocolate in cups,
   and taught to amasar tortillas
    just like tía.

In that tall-ceilinged wooden-doored house
 owned by cold drafts and toasted spaces
  chuleando magic-flamed gas heaters
   (where my thoughts are warmed
     until they have enough chiste in them
       to move.)

In that tall-ceilinged solid-floored house
 engraved with the secrets and scars of 5 generations
  and 10 ideations and a hundred inspirations
   and the shapes and the colors and the corners
    of my mind.

In that cold-windowed house
    lies a woman
  old and silent with large roving eyes
  bare beneath her clothes in a shrunken frame,
   and thin as onionskin over bones.

Her hand reaches out of a mattress
 and we discover
  she is still
   alive.

Her skin, worn so old it is almost translucent,
 absorbs us
and her organs are visible and audible
    like miracles
     she fragile-ly
       breathes.

In that tall-ceilinged house
 In that tall-ceilinged room
  with too many walls and corners to count,
   she possesses us with her eyes in her breath,
    her life in her death.

We try to move her,
   and her clothes fall aside, shedding petals,
      and we stare at her too-naked old-woman's breasts
      and are ashamed
        for her helplessness.

Her eyes search us,
   reach like arms,
      dress themselves
        and crawl out of the mattress.

We do not know what to say
   with our sight,
And her eyes begin to cover us
   with hand-made healing quilts.
They stroke us with compassion
   and they grow a shade in power.
      They move and dance
      and as I watch
      I am absorbed.
I lean over the still body, still mattress-bound,
   and wonder who she is and why I care
      so much.

In that tall-ceilinged ancient eight-walled house
   owned by cold drafts and volcanic spaces
I breathe in through her onionskin lungs
      and know,
with her eyes too old to need vision to see
      that she
        is
        me.

Caminitos

The pathways of my thoughts are cobbled with
  mesquite blocks
    and narrow-winding,
long and aged like the streets of
    san fernando de bexar
      y la villa real de san antonio
pensive
  y callados
cada uno con su chiste
  idiosyncracy
    crazy turns
that are, because they are
  centuries magic

cada uno hecho así
  y with a careful
    capricho touch,
      así

They curl slowly into ripples,
  earthy and cool like the Río Medina
          under the trees
  silently singing, standing still,
    and flowing, becoming,
      became
        and always as always,
          still fertile, laughing, loving
            alivianada
    Río Medina,
      under the trees,
        celebrating life.

They end up in the monte, chaparral,
  llenos de burrs, spurs
    pero libres
  Running through the hills freefoot
    con aire azul,
blue breaths peacefully taken
    between each lope
      remembering venado,
        remembering conejos,
      remembering
      where
        we came from.

Nací La Hija

Nací la hija
    de una hija
        de una curandera

Y la hija
    de un hijo
        de un obrero maestropastor

Mientras l'otrabuela
      crecía matas
    y l'otroabuelo
      forjaba metal.
Pues ni pa'qué preguntar porqué
    (is it any wonder then)
    frecuentemente me pongo
      a forjar remedios,
        predicando a las matas
            y
      tratando de
        curar
          metal.

Work Clothes

my father puts on his work clothes,
heavy gray trousers singing their strength,
work-blue shirt doin' dignity,
heavy, paint-splotched shoes,
with axle grease and carpenter slivers,
makin' a path.

my mother puts on her work clothes,
the housedress, spotted white
below the waist by bleach
spilt on the laundry bench
the bosom rubbed by worried arms,
special-supper gravy hands,
and tear-healed cheeks of
young grandchildren.

I go to my dresser,
check the closet,
search for that elf that
steals things that
we'll need right when
we'll miss them,
but I can't find
no good shoes
splotched with every good
project done in the last five years,
no housedress strong enough
to face the bleach without
showin' the difference,
no Sears Best-Durable
Quality tough trousers
meant to last the next two-hundred
forty-five hot washings.

just this suit worn

too many times to now,
a bit more worn on right lapel
from conference nametags' stick'um
and rough pins
and blue-ink stains around the cuffs
from rubbing notes and washing out ideas,
Walgreens drugstore's latest pantyhose
and not-too-sturdy heels
(my father never would approve of
these for painting, tune-ups,
even pulling weeds.)

But it's the same,
the story shining through the spots,
the glowing of the fabric dear,
and, through my humming and my
mental-note-path mumbling,
I can hear it singing
a good day's work ahead
like when
my father puts on his work clothes
and stands outside in the sun
ready to get serious
about this stuff
life is made of.

¡Ajay!

A hearty laugh rumbles
    and un grito mexicano — ¡Ajay!

His eyes aglow like emerald embers
    of unknown colors —
    sometimes light, sometimes dark
      always dreaming —

Sinvergüenza smile dances in to say
    "Qué raza tan más bonita"
    while his brown hands turn problems slowly
    into solutions

And his singing voice
    refuses to know the meaning
      of defeat.

y cuando pienso en tí

y cuando pienso en tí...

pienso en las olas de mares secretos
que jamás han conocido ni mentiras ni dominación
que broncos nacen y broncos bailan
y broncos viven su exaltación.

pienso en las rocas bruñidas, alisadas,
esculpidas por los siglos con la marca de amor,
de la pared más alta del castillo más viejo
en el valle lozano de mi corazón.

pienso en las jarras enterradas, vidriadas,
que, sencillas, sobreviven dueño, duelo, y civilización.
que en su obra, dan vida, y en su vida, dan gracia,
que refrescan, y cargan agua, cuento, y canción.

pienso en tus ojos, antorchas encendidas,
que regalan miradas, caminos, y calor.
pienso en planetas de lunas gemelas
de tierras perladas de raro valor.
de seres valientes de ojos danzantes
que sueñan y cambian su gema color.

pienso en tu alma de calor y coraje
ardor y justicia, viveza y amor.
pienso en cristales de eterna pureza,
diamantes ardientes de espontánea belleza
adornando cavernas de primordial creación
adornando el universo con su paz y pasión.

pienso en lo siempre de un manantial
brotando melodías y gozo y frenesí.
pienso en un viento de vida-aire sin igual
y en un eterno querer cuando pienso en tí.
      un eterno querer, cuando pienso en tí.

Oh Soft-Eyed One

Oh soft-eyed one
with your hard hunger
standing at my door
You hesitate to knock
But my ears dance already
to the song of your wet breath
wanting one place warm —
a feeding just as hard —
and melody resulting
from two voices
soft

The Minuit Chingade

Listen my children
and you shall see
how the *créme de la créme*
makes its *reverie*.

A little *français*
may nicely be *mezclée'd*
to show one's *noblesse*
and *vie sophistiquée'd*,

A sign of finesse
to chase away the *bête noir*
d'être pas different,
except with *pouvoir*.

But what a *faux pas*
if you should *sortie*
not into *français*
but the español de aquí!

Some call it Tex-Mex
some call it enchilayde
But one thing's for sure —
no sirve para nayde.

To mix Spanish in our English
would be a penda-haid.
They would *répliez* — without *s'il vous plâit* —
"*Allez a la ching-aid*."

So to be accepted
by the *aristocracie*,
Bite your tongue, hold your words,
(or to put it more simply...)

Ma chére chicanade,
watch how you parlay:
Pick *les langues de prestige*,
Avoid *les minoritées*.

And if you believe this...
Pauvre, pas de probléme,
Mais pour moi, I must confide,
Any-buey que *tout le même* ...

Every language has value,
da gusto *l'ambience* —
La langue c'est moi,
    et vive le diference!

El Mercado

— ¡Molcajetes!
Listos pa' echarles su arrozito
pa' curarlos.
Velvet pictures — pa' su sala, Señora —
Mira este tigre magnífico — o aquí —
Jesús, con su corona de espinas,
y el Presidente Kennedy
(que bueno era con los mexicanos)
pa' su comadre — la que anda muy
metida en eso de las neighborhood meetings!
"Excuse me — do you have som-bray-roes?
Those great big ones, you know?"
Chiles! Frescos (y a buen precio.)
Chile petín! Serranos! Jalapeños!
Chile colorado ya molido!
"Excuse me — are these hot?"
— It feels so hot already. Ya me anda!
My father used to call these days la canícula.
— Y la Tencha? ¿Porqué no 'stá hoy?
¿Se le falló el ride?
— ¿No oíste? iii — ¡qué tragedia!
Pos que su hermano — él que vive con ella —
se fue pa' la Social Security,
pa' que le pagaran lo de su retirement,
y que no le pueden dar nada porque su employer
no le había sacado pa' Social Security nada,
después de 40 años.
Y que le dolía el pecho
pero no quería ir con el doctor
porque decía que no tenía el conqué
y que todavía no llegaba al sixty-five
pa' Medicare —
y pos nomás se aguantó,
y ya no se quejó.
"Is it far from here to the Alamo?"
Y que ayer al regresar la Tencha a la casa,
con toda su montonota de florezotas de papel,
esas que vende ella y que les gustan
tanto a los gringos,
pos que al entrar a su casa,
cargada de todo y no viendo lo que estaba allí,
que se atropieza con el cuerpo de su hermano
en el piso, y se cae arriba dél,

con todo y flores.
y el pobre — mas muerto que —
bueno, pos la Tencha que está
para matarse con pena que why didn't she
make him go to the doctor — y habérselo pagado
ella
Qué lástima, hombre. —
Si, pobre 'e la Tencha. Oyes, si pasas por su casa,
me traes las flores y lo que tenga a mercar,
y yo se los vendo aquí,
pa' que tenga la pobre
pa' sus gastos.
— Okay, 'mano. Y el helote
y la fruta que no se venda hoy,
se la llevo — al cabo que
mañana hay otro load.
— Sí, siempre llega otro load.
a-ay, así es la vida.
— Así es la vida.
— ¡Molcajetes!
Listos pa' echarles su arrozito
pa' curarlos.

To Mr. Gabacho "Macho"

an on-the-street response

This is a different language, vato,
and you better learn it quick.
We're a talkin', Mr. Gabacho Macho
and you're scared cause I'm a spic.

You're hearin' and you're knowin'
and when it rains it pours
And just cause it's our English
doesn't mean that it is yours.

And you thought we didn't know it
and were "language disadvantaged"
And suddenly we're educated,
fluent, and de-savaged.

And there's words a pourin' out
that you never heard before
And they can't just all be Spanish
(like you learned once from that whore.)

There's words like ethnocentrism
and gross deracination
and eco-political hierarchy
and cultural exploitation.

And you're *sure* this isn't Pleasantville
or Smithville U.S.A.
Or Tom, Betty, and Susan's home
or even "Happy Days."

No, this isn't Middle America
or even upper lower...
...It's barrio town we're walkin' through
And your watch is runnin' slower.

There's hunger here and anger too,
and insult and frustration.
There's words you never heard about
like Gacho Agui-tay-shun.

No, Gacho isn't Macho
and we don't all carry knives
And our women don't all go to mass
nor our men all beat their wives.

Our men head more than welfare lines
And our women aren't so timid

And we don't steal Fritos from your bowl
or test Arrid to the limit.

Here "chili" isn't a dish with beans
It's a concentrated bowl of salsa
And my sister isn't pregnant
even though she *is* descalsa.

The only sombreros I ever saw
were on the heads of tourists
and the girl with a rose between her teeth
is working as a florist.

And no, "te aguitaste"
doesn't mean that you drank water
And "Cuida'o, porque me caliento"
doesn't mean it's getting hotter.

A project here's not what you *do*
It's where you *live*, and trust us —
when we talk about "los corts,"
we don't mean "centers of justice."

Sometimes you get the feelin'
we know this nation better'n you?
Well, Lordy me — how smart you be!
'Cause that just might be true!

This is a different language, vato,
and you better learn it quick
'Cause you see, Mr. Gabacho "Macho,"
This woman here's
                    a spic.

P   E
  O   R
   Z   B
  O   I
  L

Torn-up billboards wave goodbye
with their shreds in the wind
Rio Grande City has one stoplight.
Isn't that enough?
An empire alone
full of proud emperors and empresses
Each ruling their domain, their tecorucho, their handplow,
The birds warn on the way in — the moat of rabbits, turtles, snakes,
a winding road, coyotes, lechuzas keep out the outside world
"¿Y por qué hay discriminación contra el mexicano?" me preguntan.
A centuries-old world full of mexicanos pelirrojos,
Blondes, morenos, y ojos borrados.
Todos vienen de Rio Grande City.
O de La Grulla.
Fort Ringgold was here once.
The soldiers se cansaron
because there was nothing here to fight.
The defense of the Rio Grandeanos is complete.
La tierra, el cielo, el sol los protege.
"¿Y de qué?" preguntan. A yawn, cansancio.
Alvaro Lopez my friend disappeared once. He
left Rio Grande to see the world — college,
photography, and big cities But always came
back to take his best photographs in RioGrandeCity.
¡Lo conoces? le pregunto al señor
"Era mi sobrino
Hace un año
que desapareció
La última carta
la recibió su abuela
'taba pensando de ir a
meditar alguna parte
callada." You see
what happens to   RioGrandeanos
whostaytoolong
away from the   magic valley
They lose their
glue and   vanish
                into thin air
atom by atom
Es difícil   survive allá
cuando se han   criado en el
pozo perdido   deRioGrandeCity.
Es difícil   survive
sin   sus
coyotes brujos
que los protegen.
Aquí el aire es diferente
Y no se puede
comprar

Ya no voy tomar

"Ya no voy tomar"
dijo el tío en su cama de cruda.
"Ya no voy tomar"
dijo el tío amasándose los cesos.

Con un recuerdo neblado de una alegría bruta
Y música y risa y la guitarra de oro,
Y los ángeles en sus dedos.
Y los cielos en su voz

Y hermanos sin fronteras en la ola de la canción
Viajando juntos en el río de la vida y melodía
"¡Que bruta la crudota que me dí!" y
. . . "Ya no voy tomar"

Y se fue con sus tortillas al trabajo,
al sudor, al patrón, al dolor
de la espalda y del insulto
y de la carcel del dinero
Y se trajo sus diez pesos
al caer el sol.

Y solito, solitito se dirige a la cantina
pa' juntarse con los compas
Y mañana sabe ya
que se levantará
con la melodía dulce
y "Ya no voy tomar."

and when I dream dreams . . .

when I dream dreams,
I dream of YOU,
Rhodes Jr. School
and the lockers of our minds
that were always jammed stuck
or that always hung open
and would never close,
no matter *how* hard You tried,
we messed up the looks of the place
and wouldn't be neat and organized
and look like we were s'posed to look
and lock like we were s'posed
                    to lock.

yea, that's right
I dream of *you*
degrees later
and from both sides of the desk
my dreams take place
in your two-way halls,
Hall Guards from among us,
human traffic markers, bumps on the road
between the lanes,
to say, when we were s'posed to say,
where to turn left, where right,
and how to get where you were going —
("You'll never get to high school
speakin' Spanish," I was told)
[nice of them, they thought, to not report me,
breakin' state law, school law, speakin' dirty
          (speakin' Spanish)
and our tongues couldn't lump it
and do what they were s'posed to do.
So instead I reminded others
to button buttons
and tuck shirttails in.]

I never graduated to a
Cafeteria Guard,
who knows how they were picked.
We thought it had something to do
with the FBI
or maybe the principal's office.

So we got frisked,
Boys in one line,
Girls in another,
twice every day
entering lunch and leaving
Check — no knives on the boys.
Check — no dangerous weapons on the girls
(like mirrors,
          perfume bottles,
                deodorant bottles,
                      or teased hair.)
So we wandered the halls
     cool chuca style
     "no se sale"
     and unawares,
     never knowing
     other junior highs were never frisked
     never knowing
     what the teachers said in the teacher's lounge
     never knowing we were (s'posed to be)
     the toughest junior high in town.

And the lockers of our minds
are now assigned to other minds,
carry other books,
follow other rules,
silence other tongues,
go to other schools —
Schools of VietNam,
Schools of cheap cafe,
Schools of dropout droppings, prison pains, and
     cop car's bulleted brains.
Marcelino thought the only way
to finance college was the Air Force
(G.I. Bill and *good pay!*)
War looked easy (compared to here)
Took his chances on a college education,
Took his pay on a shot-down helicopter
in a brown-skinned 'Nam,
with a pledge of allegiance in his mind
he had memorized through Spanish-speaking teeth,
as a Hall Guard, "clean-cut"
Now — cut clean down
in a hospital ward,
paralyzed below the lips,

that still speak Spanish
slowly.
Silvia thought no one had the right
to tell her what to do.
One year out of junior high, she bitterly bore
her second pregnancy,
stabbed forks onto cafe tables
and slushed coffee through the crowds
sixteen hours a day, and she was *fifteen*
and still fighting to say
"I HAVE A RIGHT TO BE ME!"

And Lalo with a mind that could write in his sleep
growing epics from eyes that could dream
now writes only the same story
over and over
until the day
that it's *all*
over,
as he's frisked and he's frisked and he's frisked
and they keep finding
nothing
and even when he's *out*
his mind is always *in*
prison.

Like Lupe's mind
that peels potatoes
and chops *repollo*
and wishes its boredom was less
than the ants in the hill
and never learned to read because
the words were in English
and she
was in Spanish.

I wonder what we would *do*,
Rhodes Junior School
if we had all those
emblems of *you*
stamped on our lives
with a big red "R"
like the letter sweaters
we could never
afford

to buy.

I keep my honorary
junior school diploma
from you
right next to the B.A., M.A.
etcetera to a Ph.D.
because it means
I graduated
from you
and when I dream dreams,
— how I wish my dreams
had graduated too.

Compliments

They say I don't look thirty
They also say
I don't look Mexican.
They mean them, I guess,
as compliments.

If that is so,
then it must be
complimentary
to not be
thirty
or
Mexican.

Therefore,
I guess,
they don't
(as much)
like people
who are over
thirty
or too
Mexican.

But now they know
that I am
over thirty
and very Mexican,
and therefore, I guess
it means
that now
they don't
(as much)
like me.

Early Training

(Somerset, Texas 1976)

She was less than 4,
    ranchera smile and sandy feet and hands
    running over a cistern-hill to get to
    the "new" car and the "new" person
    she didn't know like most kids for a new toy.

She hung on my open car-door
    and smiled and flirted in that
    swinging, barefoot
    4-year-old way, eager on the
    edge of a giggle or a piece of "canny."

"¿Cómo te llamas?" declara.
    Le contesto y continúa
    con what will be
    her three-part questionnaire,
    viendo que esta "mushasha" (yo) tiene
    a lo menos la edad de
    un grownup —

"Tu tienes baby?"
                "No,"   (I am enjoying
                        her flirtatious
                            game.)

"Tu tienes hásban?"
                "No,"   (I notice that
                        she seems perplexed
                        and finally
                        can think of only
                        one more
                        question.)

"¿Pos qué tienes?"

Occupation: None

¡Un momento! ¡Ay voy!
Bueno, sí, Jes, hello?
Oh — soor-vey?
O-key —
Yo te lo contesto — A ver que?
Name?
Oh, sí — yo tengo name.
Mi nombre es
María Francisca Baca Gonzales Montoya de Luján.
What? You wan' to know which is my last name?
Todos, mijita, todos! All of them!
Gonzales — eso fue nombre de mi mamá.
Y Baca — mi papá....
Montoya was my gram-mo
(it is very important family, m'ijita)
And Luján — my husband's last name.

They don' fit in the line? — Pues escríbelo chiquito, m'ija!
Write little!
Ah — "H?" Eighty-Juan.
Y nacida? — O, claro que sí.
Aquí.
No! Que born en Mexico, ni que born en East L-A!
No — en Albuquerque. "Al-ba-*ker*-key, como dicen ustedes."
How long family live there?
....Abou' four hundre' years....
— we not forre-ners...¿Y tú?

Juan more question? Chur, chur, andale.
Que hago?
Pues crié familia — seis hijos — veinte nietos —
y tambíen trabajo de labor.

A ver....
Que occupation none? Cómo?
¡Oyes! Yo me levanté a las cinco de la mañana —
cada mañanita de mi vida — a veces mas temprano —
y que a hacer las tortillas, moler el chile, dar de comer
a los hombres, a los niños, a los amigos, a todos!
Y limpiar, y lavar, y enseñar a los hijos —
que whas right...y whas wrong...
y como portarse como la gente...
How to act like people!

Is hard job raising children!
Y la mayoría del tiempo ir a piscar —
Y esta espalda que está todo "bent over" así —
fue por piscar helote, y po-tatoe, y squash,
y todo lo que comes tú!
Y también en los factories cuando había necesidad,
y trabajo de aquí y allá — y trabajando a todos lados!
No, señorita!
Allí — en occupation — donde puso "none" — quítaselo.
¡Quí-ta-se-lo!
y ponlo aquí donde dice "salary."
Salary? None. Occupation — mu-u-ucho!

To Miss Celie

You stood in front a mirror
    grown woman
      n sed
I ugly I funny shape I skinny
   n you felt it
   nside yr heart
     n hurt.

N then you wen on
  n like yourself
    anyway
  n get yourself
    the color purple

N here we be
  rest of us
  grown women
stand n front a mirror
     n say
I ugly I funny shape
I too skinny I too fat
I too short I too dark
   n we feel it
   nside our hearts
      n hurt

 but you give us
   the color purple
   n it dance all over us
so we go on ahead
   n like ourselves anyway
   n laugh

   cuz we know the mirror,
   — it funny shape too.

19 años

de niña fue pachuquita, valiente, chocante, peleonera
    y nadie le decía qué hacer.
    nunca le habían conquistado.

a los 14 años le echaron de la escuela
    pudiera haberse quedado
    pero no se iba dejar
    y no iba dejarle a nadie
                insultarle.
se quedó en la casa, ayudándole a mamá
                cuidando los hermanitos.
Se aburría. También pasaba mucho tiempo
a la esquina con Rudy y Mando, platicando, flortiando.
    Mando tan chocante como siempre,
        Rudy tan dulce.
            (¡pero que vato el Mando!)

a los 15 se puso pregnant. No supieron
    sus padres. Nomás les decía que tenía
    dolor de estómago. Querían mandartraer a
    la Doña Chuchita, que se lo curara, pero ella resistía
    Tampoco le dijo al Mando.
    Alcabo que él ya se estaba portando bien frío
    y pasando mucho tiempo con la hija de Marta Perez.
    Una vez ella se puso bien mal;
    perdió el bebito — así sin nacer el pobrecito.
        Pos mejor — que alcabo el pobre hombrecito no
        tuviera...
            Bueno,... — Nomás no tuviera.

Pasó un año. No salía mucho. Se quedaba en la casa
    pensando de muchas cosas.
    Regresó el Mando. Quería verla a la esquina.
    Ella no quiso, pero...
    fue. Con su carro nuevecito se creía muy chingón.
    Puro papel. — Ella no se dejó amadrear.
    Adentro se sentía bien gacho —
    todavía dolía, pero no le dejó ver eso.
    Se hizo que no le importaba —
    bien fresca. Ya comenzó a portarse bien feo él.
    La 'staba lastimando. Comenzó a forzarla.
    Luchó pero él estaba muy fuerte...

Regresó a la casa llorando.

A los 19 la conocí, trabajando en una fonda
que ni era la más
limpia ni la más sucia.
Recibiendo ni demasiados
ni muy pocos. Haciendo su salario.
Pasándola.
Tenía una fuerza y una mirada
que le hacía más
mujer que la mayoría de las que ganan su
"respeto" en otros lugares.
Otros tipos de prostitutas
Prostitutas elegantes, prostitutas respetadas,
prostitutas del prestigio, prostitutas del dinero —
    presidentas de prostitutas, reinas de prostitutas,
        y toda la alta sociedad.

    Pero ella era más mujer —
        más mujer que todas. Ella vendía
        sus horas.
        Otras vendían
        sus vidas.

Me dijo:

"Es que ya me cansé. Ahora —
Nadie me va decir qué hacer — nadie. Ahora tengo
yo el control.
Sí. Me hacen lo que les de la gana.
Pero porque yo, yo digo.
Yo decidí que iba dejarlos.
Porque yo, yo dije
Por eso, me tienen miedo.
Porque ellos chinguichinguichingui
y a pesar de todo, saben
que yo tengo el control final.
Por tanto que me chingan de afuera,
    no me pueden chingar el corazón."

in the wash

You said you believed in women
   and women's forward progress,
   but that wasn't it —
      you only believed in yourself,
       and not too kindly.

I can still see you,
puffing arrogantly,
Always uncomfortable with virgins,
because they had not been owned.
You said it was because
you once got a spot of blood
on your new white linen suit
   but that wasn't it —
        (Any woman could have told you
        that blood comes out in the wash
        though not easily.)

You said it was because
of your guilt about my loving you
when you no longer loved me
that you wished to break it off
(but didn't)
   But that wasn't it —
      it was just your
      fear of loving
      and of love
      that had you always keeping me
      a bit denied, a bit
      enslaved, a bit
      held off.

When I didn't call you (finally)
for more than two weeks,
and you knew (finally)
something was wrong
and you called me
to ask if we
could "really spend some time"
You said it was because
I at last realized
that I no longer loved you
and you could (now) feel free from
guilt at not loving me

and that *that's* why
you wanted me.
    But that wasn't it —
        it was because
        you were afraid
        that you had (finally) lost me.

And you said (later, I'm sure) it
was because I was
"the marrying type," and needed some
"security" that I had left you
as you glanced nervously
at my ring finger
to see if someone had
"purchased" my allegiance.
(and found they hadn't.)

But that wasn't it —
    that wasn't it at all.
        it was all those spots
        covering your heart,
        covering your eyes,
        covering your life,
        cutting off (finally)
        my love.
And I
met a man
who didn't hide
from himself

And I'm certain
there's plenty things you say
about that now,
    but none of them are it —
        and all of them
    come out
    in the wash
    (though, unlike that first spot
        of blood
        that frightened you so
        for the mark it left on you,)

            easily.

Autumn Planet

You squeak on your axle,
   worn from all our games
the hair of your poles
   is falling out
   and leaving
   your head unprotected
   and you
   too often
   too feverish
   and yet strangely
   unwarmed by the sun
   even on the hottest day

there are parts of you
   that are infertile and
   struggle to bear fruit
   and parts that struggle even
   to digest the same day's food
you spit out teeth daily
   into space,
and erupt burps and gas
   that knock people aside
   and make you
   hard to live with,
   as your color
   changes, and your breath
   sours

Yet your eyes are always
   lightning with youth,
   dreaming stubbornly still,
   shining from us
      all
   at once.

Rain Seeds

Rain seeds
like drops of cool beginning
kiss earth in soft silence
and treasure-cradle
hidden underneath the grass,
their secret song, sweet whispered, saved.
Like drops of hope from my lips,
they study each slow unborn sun
and await the time
      to sprout.

Casa

The comal smells like flour tortillas
   even when it's not
The jardín de hierba (casi) buena grows
   como si fuera este cualquier barrio mexicano
   ni fijándose de los rednecks
The wildflowers (mojadas) cross over (sin papeles)
   and move in with us
Y de pronto aparecen mil chamaquillos de la vecindad
   growing like arbolitos
   in our front yard

You wear manhood
   like sunlight.
And mi vientre (¡maceta chiflada!)
   se hincha
      queriendo, como las ciruelas
         del arbol

      cargar semilla

       también.

Scars and Three Daughters

she handed me a lotion
her grandmother had
handed her — this grown
daughter, strong and
armied, always smiling,
not born to me but rather
married to me, full with her brother
and her father — and her good
heart. "Concha Nacar," magic
cream, that "one light dab
touched on every day
will soften scars and make
them blend away."
I rush to put it on
the face of that black-diamond-eyed
power pack, my three-year-old
invincible returning hero
from a scratch of cat, a brush with tree,
her will untroubled by
the fear of scars,
I trembling take the potion,
pray the cream like incantations on
that face that I adore
want to preserve, protect, insure
yet I stare proudly at that thin white line
on hand that I have come to know as me,
that crooked intersection on the cheek
that I have loved to teasing say
came from a switchblade scar,
my "football knee" I brag
was an old "childcare injury"
while rushing to avoid a baby fall
as she charged forth, so ready to explore,
and that most precious line of all —
that now-pink redscar
where the firstborn love was passed,
still sleeping in her sac,
and left me only this
to touch her with —
I love my scars
would never wipe them out
don't mind the eldest fading hers,
the firstborn leaving hers as mark,

or me protecting mine
like document or memory or family property,
but — black-diamond-treasure,
smooth as beauty jewel-hardening in the sun
and polished clean
when will I learn
to bear your scars
and let you keep them
as your history
unveiled

Of Beer And Sofas (or Frank's Dilemma)

Pancho Villa sits on the faded sofa —
   Herculon Sears-Special first round
   but then, through the *Austin-American,*
   second round, good deal, and still in
   pretty good
   shape
   except for the see-through spot
   on the left
   arm —
drinking a Coors light (Tecate's too
expensive and they're
out of Schlitz)
and says "I don't know. I just don't know."
He's talking to Reyes Cardenas —
only one you can still
trust these
days
(although he'll write about you —
he'll always write about you —
things that sound strange and raise
eyebrows
make people look at you weird
  — chiches sticking out of flying saucers, erect;
     vaginas in laundromats, everything's wet and somehow...Tokyo
     — but nobody understands anyway and trust is still
     trust
)

Frank is wondering where to
go
Got a letter asking "Mr. Villa" to apply,
but those are getting fewer these days
and almost always end up political
traps
Aztec sacrifices to gringo gods
The whole thing's messed
up
Like the good black cop on Days of Our
Lives
don't know who to trust —
    not the chief, *forsure*, linked up with
       money, drugs and Big Scale Politics (crime) —

"I don't know.

I just don't know.
It's easier to pinpoint an
enemy outside

but
it's not there
somehow it all comes
down
to the universe in
here.

here.
The good, the bad, the struggle is all in
side
And I wish Ghandi'd liked
Tecate — then we could've really
talked
And maybe figured something
out
Cause Zapata was always
too much of a hero
    and heroes sell out to the movies
    and the legends all the time
He coulda used more foolin' aroun'
shoulda gotten married every month
like I did
Woulda made the movies look less
sexy to him

And Madera was a good guy —
a fine guy —
like Tomás Rivera —
but didn't *play* enough
Was too human
and it got to 'im.

Then there were the egos —
Corkys and Angels and Ricardos (or Richards),
better versions of Ronald Reagan;
John Wayne
    from the other side

And I loved'm all —
but I didn't always like'm
And I don't like at all
where we
are
."

Reyes makes a joke or two
and writes another poem
And Pancho, feelin' comftrbl,
keeps thinking it out
fingering it, like the bare spot on the threads,
where you can see a little sponge on the other side,
and that feels kinda honest, and really looks better n better all the time

"If Marta Cotera had gotten to me in time,
I'd a done something more than just *marry* the women,
Hell, I'd a bought'm beer,
and married *myself*!
Hung «Frank and Panchita»
over the door and
maybe really learned something. Hell, I'da married
everybody —
Ghandi and Juarez and Emma Tenayuca
the viejito who sells paletas
and la abuela de los welfare kids
Henry B. and Henry Cisneros
the young Iranian students and the KGB-CIA
Pope John Pole and Duarte and Fidel
Even the gringos —
Princess Di and Madeleine Murray O'Hare,
Richard Nixon and Richard Rodriguez —
and échale — Cheech an Chong, and La Malinche — Ajáy! —
We'd a gathered them all together in
a giant Hall and pronounced
the vows — hell, I'd a even married *you*, Reyes —
and *you* got buck teeth and gray hair!"

I guess it reminded him, cause Pancho
started stroking the grey hairs
que se le estaban saliendo,
not certain whether to be proud of'm or believe this year's
commercials
He decided to do both
and laughed.

"Oyes, Reyes," he complains, feelin' good,
"You talk too much!"

"Wanna help me write up los
invitations?
There'll be an awful lot."

— Chingones, — says Reyes, always

laughing quiet.

"Knowing you, it'll be a poem
about the Eiffel Tower
unzipping his pants."

— Her pants. —

"Orale."
Pancho Villa takes another swig of beer, slow and
comfortable, not moving.
This one's generic, and not bad.

The slow aging, rubbing, of the couch
continues.
He can now see
the sponge
pretty clear.

Letter to Ti

*— From Le Van Minh, 15 and Amerasian, after arriving
in the U.S. from Viet Nam, having spent the last four years
surviving being fed by and carried on the back of a friend
called "Ti."*

It is strange being here
like yellow fog wrapped softly around a dream.
The wrapping paper comes undone
and inside I see my face
reflected.
Now, I do not try to look less American.
I should try to look less Vietnamese.
But most times, I just rest,
and don't try anything at all.
The time to close one's eyes is good here
Except that I see you,
the stiff hairs on the back of your neck
laying flatter
with the sweat,
your hard breathing and your bony shoulders
body-friends to my riding body.
As much as I loved your eyes,
the back of your neck was just as dear to me,
the straining neck smiled just as much,
the light shone from around your ears
like the gentle friendship of your face
looking at me.
I knew your neck better than anyone.

Many carry me here.
There will be a chair too
in which I can carry myself.
I eat every meal.
I am in a bed at night.
People do not laugh at me
for my features,
my spine or legs.
I no longer make paper flowers.

I unwrap gifts from people I do not know.
The wrapping paper falls aside.
Sometimes I pick it up and fold it curve it
lay my cheek against it.
"Are you making flowers?" they ask me.

"No.
A neck.
The back of a neck,
Four years my home...
and still."

MotherMother

(they see Hiroshima and speak of nuclear "defense")

Earth —

Your womb has been

cut open

just as mine
just as my mother's

Your child has died

in its halo of innocence

just as mine
just as my mother's

Your heart has pounded

angry, crying beats

in slaughtered grasps
for the child...
for your
soul

and drummed slowly

by the gravesite

in time to the warm pulse
of the rocking wind
which lulls
the child's
tomb.

Now —

That child is gone
That cut is mended

But let us

save

the next.

Walking the Dreampoem

I too have been stripped clean to the bone
growing silent amid the cries of the unbarked
left unsheathed in honesty,
cracking with the give of the wood of past generations
and aging with the memory of their voices.

I too have been taken to the earthfire
camped on my own essence and my own entrails
bowed, aching, scorched,
    and shorn my leaves windlessly
    living mouth-to-mouth with the breath of breaking.

I too have been bent to the wind,
rubbed naked in its wake
scarred through seven years' rings
and dying many times alone.

Yet so between the forest of the birch
and the birches in their fall
    your chant surfaces,
        dark and squirming newborn
    through the echo of the years,
        trying still to be helpless.

But the mountains have grown strong surrounding me,
I am different now
The spirits are too clear
to be washed away by rain
or hidden by green leaves.

I too have been stripped clean to the bark,
growing silent among the cries of the unborn,
left unsheathed in honesty
        and wonder

But the wood of my chest has grown and aged in tune,
in time, fully to its natural bent,
and the twigs decide whether to break under me
as I go walking the dreampoem through the present.

those things that were said to us

where go those things
that were said to us
and not heard
where go those words
that were almost whispered
from the thirsty tongue
cracked grey with crust of death
where go those messages
the mouth could not quite form
shaped around a groan
and we could not make out
but we saw the rolling eyes
and heard the tone
untold

where go those things
that were said to us?
In the morning,
the body is placed in the ground,
the flutter of the eyes
still echoing in my mind,
and by evening,
soft raindrops resting sentry,
the swallows have returned
home
to the earth-bricked Mission.

Fighting Paper

All my life

I've been

   fighting paper

      "I'm sorry but you do not have the proper
      papers we have no record of
      papers authorizing you to present these
      papers these are only the exact duplicates of the original
      papers we need exact duplicates these
      papers do not match the other
      papers these papers carry different first names
                  (But I have two names) these
      papers carry different addresses (But I moved) these
      papers carry watermarks wrong these
      papers have their margins wrong these
      papers do not have a seal these
      papers need notarization, verification, authentication
      papers cannot be issued to you unless you already have
      papers

The Great Wall of Vellum
locks me
out
me acuerdo de la luz
en ojos de papá
cuando él decía
(sabio sin intentar)
           "puro papel"
and spit his proof of falsity
  with saliva
  but not too far
hedging wise
never getting too near
the papeles

Still
   I fight you
   daily courtesan who will not

      quit

   for all I want to do

   with you, papel,

is take you

fresh and peaceful,

clean, of morning,

    full of past
and new, like earthy present,

to plow softly into you,

    furrows of crumbling
        readiness

    plant the words gently in your warmth

      so that you might

          — at last —

            bear

            fruit.

III.
Selected Short Stories

Chencho's Cow

It all began when Chencho's cow kicked over a pot of beans. The very pot of beans that Chencho had so painstakingly prepared the night before for the Amados' baby's celebration, selecting the beans with care, cooking them on a low fire for hours, with salt, chile, and bacon, then putting in the *tomate*, *cilantro*, onions, and more bacon near the end, with, of course, the crowning touch — a can of beer — to make them *frijoles borrachos*, little drunk beans that he would ladle up into small cups that people would down like chocolate syrup, only better, not leaving even a teaspoonful of juice at the bottom, and always going back for more.

It was a special occasion. Elena and Javier Amado had given birth to a round-cheeked boy whom they named Carlos Javier, after both their fathers; and Chencho, their neighbor, was invited to the gathering at the house after the baptism. In fact, he was on the way to the party with the aromatic pot of beans cradled in potholders when he heard the cow "moo" loudly and decided to make certain she still had enough water, since he didn't know how late the party would keep him.

It was for being in a rush (as problems usually are) that he laid the pot down so close to her, thinking just to run the hose a minute and continue on his way. But the smell of those delicious drunk beans must have made the cow more energetic than usual, and when Chencho turned around to pick up the hose, she followed him, kicking over the beans and all their *jugo* onto the thirsty dirt. Chencho found himself in a true quandary. He wanted to go to the party, but he wanted to take a pot of beans with him. He thought about making up some quick *papa con huevo*, or squeezing some juice into a large *galón* bottle, but that wasn't what he wanted to take. He wanted to take a pot of beans. Worse than that (the truth had to be told), he wanted to take *that* pot of beans — the very pot he had made with young Carlos Javier Amado in mind, and that now lay flavoring the red, sandy dirt. He stared at it, he *wished* it back into the pot, he even thought about scooping up what he could, but one look at the cow (and one smell) changed his mind. There was simply nothing that could be done.

The party was as pleasurable as imagined. The townspeople were happy to congratulate (and toast) the young child. Everyone understood about the beans, and they all agreed with Chencho that it was a terrible shame. Chencho took his accordion and played for the party, and even promised the young couple a replacement pot of beans for the next Sunday round of visitors. Everyone went home feeling good. Everyone except Chencho.

Every day for a week, he would go out into the barn and stare at the floor, jealously remembering that pot of beans. It got to the point where he began to neglect his fields, and he even shouted angrily at his cow one day. He apologized to her, but still it bothered him — it even bothered him that it bothered him.

One morning, as Chencho was standing in the barn heaving one of his now-customary sighs, someone said, "It doesn't have to happen that way, y'know." Behind him stood an *avena*-faced Anglo, a man dressed formally and all in black, like one of those *Protestante* ministers, hat coolly in hand. The man pointed to where Chencho's beans had by now (Chencho was sure) fertilized and strengthened the ground with their nutrients. "Such a waste and all for no necessary reason," said the stranger.

Chencho was startled a bit and also a little embarrassed, as if someone had caught him without his clothes on. "My beans?" Chencho verified, his discomfort not permitting any more eloquent a response than that. "Mm-hm," the stranger nodded, and looked coolly at the rim of his hat.

"You heard about my beans?" Chencho asked.

"Mm-hm."

A moment of silence passed between them, their wandering eyes missing each other's intentionally.

"Hate to see you feelin' so bad, m'friend."

Funny the way the gringos, especially this kind that travelled through and appeared from nowhere, leaving also into nowhere, liked to call you "my friend," even though they had never laid eyes on you before and you didn't even know their name. He felt so irritated and embarrassed that this stranger should know so much about him. He tried to retract from that intimacy, awkwardly, but in a definite retreat.

"I'm alright." His embarrassment and the mutual silence belied his attempt. Chencho took a few steps to the side, and then — thinking better — to the front. The gringo looked away politely.

"It's just that they were for a very special fiesta . . . in the home of my young neighbors . . . the baby boy was named after his two grandfathers — very fine men, very well-respected . . ." Chencho realized he was rambling and stopped.

"Sure, nothin' the matter with that. Just bein' proper. Anyone could understand that." Chencho relaxed. The man continued, cautiously, "All the same, it do prove a bother, given everythin'." Chencho's brows came together as he studied the talkative gringo. "An' the most bothersome part comes down to just one thing — " Chencho was caught. No one had talked to him about it with such concern since the day after the party, as if everyone else had forgotten or worn out the interesting part of it, and Chencho had only himself to talk it over with. "Just one thing, m'friend, at the root of it all — causing you this heartache —" the gringo held the moment, letting Chencho hunger for an answer, "— Passion! Jus' plain passion!"

¡Gringo entremetido! Chencho thought, I knew he was sticking too far into my private feelings!

"Now don't go backin' off, m'friend. This is a problem common to the majority of human bein's that inhabit this planet! An' to darn near all of the animals! Why that cow of yours just got so excited by the smell o' those beans that she jus' had to kick up her heels an' dance across the floor behind you, kickin' over those special beans o' yours. You'd a thought she would've stepped over logically, or waited till you got the water filled an' was out o' the way, but she jus' got so filled up with passion." Chencho was listening again. "Passion's what did it! Why, people go near all their lives gettin' their feelings hurt or broodin' over things, cause o' the trouble that passion causes'm . . ."

By the time he cleared the dishes off the lunch table, Chencho was feelin' pretty good. The gringo had brought in a couple of bottles of elixir from behind the panels of his truck (to cleanse the body after eating, he said) and Chencho was feeling more relaxed than he'd been in a week, with the drone of the gringo's voice putting him just a little (but not too much) to sleep. It never occurred to him to ask what could be done about it; it just somehow made more sense for this whole incident to have had some reason. But the gringo was on his way to some special road, "If only they didn't have their hearts gettin' in the way all the time, so much could be accomplished . . ."

*   *   *

Chencho didn't remember having really thought about it a lot. In fact, he didn't really remember how it all happened. But his cow seemed to be doing fine, and the gringo reassured him that she was actually doing better than she ever had before. Even the scar where her heart had been taken out didn't seem to bother her. And the gringo was sure to point out that she would never again moo at him crossly when Chencho was late to feed or milk her. In fact, she would never again moo at him at all. There was simply no reason to do so.

There was still the matter of Chencho staring at that special spot in the barn and savoring not only the memory of the beans, but of the whole *celebración* as he had envisioned it, but the gringo had an idea that he said would take care of that, too. It wasn't that Chencho had so much confidence in the gringo — he was a curious sort that did too much talking and not enough waiting — but it was just that the man had a way of getting him to agree without asking his opinion.

"Passion! M'friend, without our hearts, we could get so much more done, and with so much less pain. Now, I wouldn't recommend this to ya' if I didn't happen to have seen it work so many times. If we weren't so emotional, we'd have lots more space for being logical. Why the proof o' that's women, ain't it? Get so emotional they don't have an ounce o' logic in'm. Now that's one that a good man like you can really understand, can't ya?" he said, laughing and elbowing Chencho. Chencho didn't, but he laughed anyway, from the mouth outwards, as they say in Spanish, but enough to keep from looking too unmasculine to the gringo.

*   *   *

This time, Chencho insisted on taking the night to think about it. He would have put it off much longer, but the gringo said he had appointments to keep in another town and would have to leave this town "sooner than I'd like, m'friend." Chencho talked about it plenty with his neighbors, and some of the things Nilo said got him so upset that he spent the whole night struggling with his pillow, and by morning was ready to give it a try, just to get rid of this problem. He went out to the barn, where the cow was standing, looking very peaceful and unconcerned. "You'd be considered quite a man to have that kind of calm and strength in every situation." Chencho turned to look at the gringo, and something about the man's absoluteness, stark black and white against the brown of the barn, made Chencho want to trust him, want to really make his "m'friend" expression a reality. He was a little nervous about the cutting part, but the gringo explained that the reason the wound had healed so rapidly on the cow (in fact, it was not even like a wound at all) was that nothing really biological had been removed, only the emotional mass, the heart itself, and without the bother of this too-emotional muscle in its chest, the body could proceed with even greater health, allowing the brain to take over the functions previously so poorly supervised by the heart.

* * *

Maybe it was Marta's grandfather, the one with the weak heart, that did it first, after Chencho, or maybe it was la rica, the one who was always so scared of someone stealing the blue tile birdbath that she'd bought in Mexico and placed so precisely in the perfect shady spot in her garden. No one seemed to remember how it had all happened, but they did recall that there were long lines in front of Chencho's house and that everyone went in very envious and excited and admiring how well Chencho and the others seemed to be doing, and came out looking very happy, or maybe it was strong, or in control, they weren't certain which. At any rate, by the time three suns had set, there wasn't a normal-brained person over the age of ten that hadn't had their heart removed by the kind gringo who brought them the science of "depassionization," as he called it. Chencho's mother had been one of the last to agree, and most of those three days she ranted and raved (quite passionately, proving the gringo's point) against the whole idea, saying that if God had meant people not to struggle for anything, he would have given women "labor thoughts" instead of labor pains. The strangest thing of all was that the reason she probably gave in and had it done was because of passion itself! She just couldn't stand to see everyone else in such a predicament and her not right in there with them, with her hands in the masa, so to speak.

Chencho's mother had made certain, before placing herself defiantly in that line, however, that her retarded niece, Eva, would not be touched. The gringo agreed emphatically, stating that it really wouldn't work well on the mentally unfit or on children under ten because, with as little as they'd accumulated up top, they wouldn't have anything left to lean on.

It wasn't until weeks after the gringo left that they realized something was missing. At first, they thought they were just forgetting things, making a mistake or two, or having a dull day. But the pattern was noticeably repeated. Their thinking no longer seemed as sharp, and the reasons for thinking things out were not known. Many things left a taste of not having been tasted. Chencho discovered that he no longer remembered how to make beans. This was the case with numerous things: they had to look elsewhere to find what had once been inside of them. Chencho contacted a cousin in a neighboring city and made clear the level of his need. The necessary papers were sent promptly. Chencho would focus all of his attention, following the directions with great care. Each step was outlined elaborately. Cleaning the beans required spreading them on the table, removing the stones, removing the beans that were shriveled more than twice as much as the majority, eliminating those that had a very dark color — correction, those that had an unnaturally dark color. (He had wondered what was unnatural, and had been told to remove those that looked burnt and reddish, while leaving those that were dark in the same shade as the dark spots on the light beans.) It seemed so complex. He had first learned to clean the beans as a child, but he had not learned with his head. He had learned with his heart, while watching his grandmother do that which had later become integrated into his view of life. Now, it was integrated into nothing more than the piece of paper he studied so thoroughly, stumbling through the applications.

"Wrinkles that come with life, wrinkles from rubbing against other beans, wrinkles from wilting under the sun — all right. Wrinkles of petrified stone — no." He worked at it repeatedly, adding precisely measured amounts of ingredients at precisely timed stages. Chencho found that every time he cooked beans, he needed to follow the written instructions again. It was as if there was some ingredient missing, but he had no idea what to add.

Chencho and the others would sit in the evenings, trying to piece together those things that their hearts could no longer provide. Eva, the retarded thirty-five-year-old, began to play a special role. She was the one they turned to for lessons in how to cuddle babies and how to help the older children play. They listened carefully as she and the little children laughed, trying to imitate the sound.

They tried to make lists of what it was they had lost, had had, and had been said in those days of the gringo's visit. They tried to piece together old conversations, but, somehow, every conversation had something important missing between the lines. The eight- and nine-year-olds were brought in to listen and respond, but even their responses were difficult to comprehend. The teenagers just took notes. Chencho's mother proposed they go over every event and every conversation from the day of the gringo's arrival to the day of his departure. Chencho remembered him climbing into the truck with some salutation, what was it? The children offered possible expressions until the right one was found. "Goodbye, my friend," the gringo had said, as he folded the worn dollar bills into his pocket. "And then what?" asked Jorge, as the Amados' baby began to cry and the adults turned to stare at him. "He wants his bottle," said a bright-eyed seven-year-old.

Chencho thought carefully, and found the information as best he could through his passionless brain. "And then he told me how fortunate we would be — to be able to work longer days in the sun, without feeling upset, and to bring home paychecks of any amount at all, without wanting to cry." "What?" asked Elena, thoroughly confused, "Without wanting to cry?" "Yes, that's what he said." "Is that all?" asked his mother, whom people somehow sensed should be regarded as a leader, although they were not certain why. "No," said Chencho slowly, "There was something more . . . something . . . like that, like what that child just did." "He laughed?" asked the seven-year-old. "Yes, that was it. He laughed. He laughed," Chencho verified, "And then he drove off."

In the distance, Chencho's cow could be heard moving around the barn, her bell dangling against the trough as she searched for food, but everyone knew that she would never again bother to moo.

You Don't Know Marta

Now, I might as well be honest and tell you right now that I'm prejudiced. I think San Antonio is the absolute center of the universe —*el mero mero ombligo*— which doesn't make me too popular livin in Austin. Now, most folks get up to Austin an say, "Isn't Austin just great?!" and "Don't you *love* it here?!" But these San Antonians just shrug their prejudiced shoulders an say, "Well, it isn't San Antonio, but . . ."

Well now, Ernie and I moved to Austin right after we got married (that is, we moved to the San Antonio side of Austin), and we hadn't been there long enough for the *cilantro* to bloom when someone at work invited him to a *tardeada*. Said a *tardeada* was an annual function to gather together the leaders of the Chicano community — a time to relax, drink beer, eat *fajitas*, let their hair down, an jus' talk. They wanted a chance to bring together all the leaders of the Mexican-American community and let great ideas be born.

Now, when he said that, I immediately thought of Marta Cotera. Marta is one of the few people I know who stays awake nights just *plotting* how to help people. Ernie has a favorite saying about Marta — he says if Marta stepped outside the city limits, the average IQ of the city of Austin would drop by 15 points. Now, you knowing about all those university professors an' high-tech researchers in Austin (not to mention some of the smartest political fananglers you ever saw in that Good Ole Boys Club they call the Capitol), you might think that was a slight exaggeration, but then you don't know Marta.

Y'know, Marta an I had plotted many a community project together, an I can vouch that we'd no sooner be sketching out the final objectives to one project than she'd be thinking up four other *spinoff* projects as well, and plannin' forty ways to get funding and implementation for all five. She jus' doesn't *stop. Mas viva que una víbora*, and goin' faster'n the speed of light, on a *slow* day. Well, so Ernie turns to me'n says, "Whaddya think? Should we go?" An both of us bein' the shy retiring type who *never* get involved in Chicano community affairs, we're both out the door before the *comal* is even cool.

We drove up to the place (a real pretty clubhouse-type place up in Zilker Park, with a nice view and the breeze blowing cool an *perfect* for a *tardeada* on a summer evening) an got out of the car, following the *mariachis* to the door. Right away, we knew something was wrong.

Now there was Marta's husband, Juan, standing with a group of five or six men, and behind them was another group of eight or nine men. Off to their right was a group of nine or ten men, to their left, a group of eight or nine men, an then maybe sixty men off on the plaza section. Now that comes to a total of ninety-four men (at a rough count), an every single one of them (or at least ninety-three) starin' at me like I was the scourge of the earth. Also, starin at Ernie like he was a cross between Aaron Burr and the assassin of Pancho Villa. Now these weren't strangers, mind you — among those ninety-three were a good thirty that were well-beknownst to us — Andrés, who teaches at the university, Ramón, another famous bilingual educator — why even good ole

Gonzalo — model Mexican-American politician an would-be *Texas Monthly* coverboy, an' every single one of'm scared *to death* to say hi or even move an *eyelid* at us!

Yeah, I said ninety-three. Number ninety-four was Arnulfo. Now, they don't call Arnulfo, Arnulfo for nothin. His face just brightened when he saw Ernie an me (two of his favorite people) and, totally unself-consciously, he came over an' shook our hands — *both of us* — like we were real human beings or something! Now I know this is hard to believe, that in the middle of that bunch of squinty-eyed thorns there would be an ole' cactus flower like Arnulfo, but there he was, big as day, smilin so bright an purty, and pumpin out his handshake like he didn't *see* the thousand eyes glued to our leprous presence. (Now, I can't say for certain, cause you *do* know that Arnulfo wears real thick glasses, and maybe it was just because of that, or maybe it was the glasses he always wears on his soul that gives him a different sight from everyone else.) At any rate, we spent twenty minutes talkin' to Arnulfo (cause he just wouldn't let us go, y'know), an then we decided we really felt like goin' on home.

Well, later on, when I ran into Andrés, he made a point of tellin' me he "agreed" with us (whatever that meant) and how they'd been told that MABPWA (that's the Mexican-American Business and Professional Women's Association) had been planning to *crash* the *tardeada*, and warned that anyone caught speaking to any woman there wouldn't be invited back the next year. Or ever again.

An ole Gilbert (of Gilbert's Office Supply and the Mexican Chamber of Commerce), seein' as how we just hadn't *known* any better, came around to invite Ernie the next year and to explain how they were planning to host "something for the ladies, sometime — a dinner or something, y'know, so they can be involved, too." An Ernie just smiled and said, "Well, you just let us know when you do, and we'll both be there." An then we took that fancy engraved invitation to the "All-Male *Tardeada*, No Women, No Anglos allowed" an just put it at the bottom of our stack of bills paid. We'd already been to *one* tardeada, an if you think all the leaders were there, then you just don't know Marta.

Quality Literature

— Dr. Dumont? — said a quiet voice from the back row of the World Lit class, as the bell rang and the distinguished professor collected his papers to dash from the room.

— Yes? — said Dumont in his crisp, pseudo-British accent, as a hazy face with a name he didn't remember approached him.

— You said the other day, that, uh, we could write our critique-thing on any author, just to get it approved by you first, and I, well, I was in the library the other day, and they got this real good book by Elena Martínez called *La Tierra Grita*, and I wanna do mine on that.

— Elena Martínez? I don't recall the name — is she the poetess from Chile?

— No, sir. She's a Chicana, and it's about a campesino family in —

— It's Chicano Literature? No, I'm afraid I just can't approve that. Read it if you wish, but for your report, we need quality literature, and Chicano literature simply isn't *quality*.

— But this stuff's good! I mean, it's the first stuff I ever seen that really talks about real things. There's writers like Toribio Salinas, and — have you read Mike Hernandez, sir?

— No, but why don't you look into Samuel Beckett's *En Attendant Godot*? The French existentialist theater is really superb in its handling of the alienation of the individual in society. It speaks to the commonest of situations, and yet elevates to the philosophically *sublime* the lowest of human positions. I would think it would be an excellent topic for you.

— But have you read Inéz de León?

— No, but I really think Beckett's French existentialist theater would provide an almost unlimited opportunity for development and commentary. I have some books that might interest you on it — now there's one by Fontaine on the peculiar juxtaposition of characters in *Godot*, and there's quite a few references available on the manneristic existentialism evident in Beckett's theater. I'm certain our library would have quite a good bit on it and —

— Well how about Frank Sanchez, sir? Have you read him?

— No, but there simply hasn't *been* any quality Chicano literature. If you must have something in Spanish, try Darío or Borges or Cervantes. Darío has been highly acclaimed in Madrid, and even Paris — said the professor, examining with slight curiosity the face of the student whom he now faintly recalled as having made very poor marks on the last exam. "Of course," he thought.

— Soledad Cantú has been published in Spain. Could I write on her, sir?

Dumont continued to shake his head, gathered his papers under his arm, leaned into the face of the student, and stated emphatically, "But it hasn't even been critiqued in the PMLA! And until it's critiqued in the PMLA, I can't say it's quality literature!"

And the professor walked off into a semi-colon...as the face of the student became an epic poem.

El Mojado No Existe
(an excerpt from the novel, *La Gente*)

Diamante crumpled up the piece of paper and propped it between the logs. She had found it blowing in the wind in front of the sheriff's office and had saved it to help start the fire this evening. There. It would soon be hot enough to cook the soup. She stared out at the sun and decided it would not be long before her younger brothers and sister would come in from their play, asking for food and asking when Papá would be home. She hurried her steps, her ten-year-old eyes keeping watch over the sun. As she was almost done, there was a knock on the door. Her face brightened when she saw José Silva. "Buenas tardes."

"Buenas tardes, José. My father is not here yet, but he would love for you to join us for supper."

"No, gracias, señorita. I must return to the ranch to finish some chores."

(*Esos Steubens agarrados*, she thought, they barely give him a few hours a week to leave the ranch.)

The young *mojado* from the Steuben ranch pulled a small doll made of straw from behind his back. "And this is for you, young lady."

She started to gasp in surprise, but caught herself and said politely, "Muchísimas gracias. Won't you come inside?"

José walked over to the fire and sat on a small stool nearby. Diamante always tried to impress José — he was so kind and so *simpático*. Sometimes, she wondered how he could be so brave — all alone, a *mojado*, far from his family. She had her family right here all the time — her father and the three younger siblings her parents had given her before Mamá passed away. She was silent for a moment — missing that strong, gentle woman who used to comb her hair into neat braids and make her soft dolls out of handkerchiefs. José saw the young girl fingering the straw doll sadly, her fingernails combing the straws on its rough yellow head. He wiped the tear off her cinnamon-milk cheek, and she quickly remembered his presence and pulled to her full height, saying, "Your gift was very kind. I'm certain the children will enjoy it, too." He started to tousle her hair, but the child had pulled on her strength and her maturity, and he did not wish to ruin her show, so he simply tipped his hat and said, "Señorita, I will check to see if your father is coming down the road yet."

By the time José Silva and Daniel Ibarra had reached the door, Diamante had the served plates on the table for her father and his hesitant young guest. She listened with great interest to their talk, her little girl crush on the young man shining through her eyes.

"I still say they hardly pay you enough for a week's work, much less a month's. And I've seen the way they treat you."

José tried to soften the subject and convince his friend that he was satisfied. "I get my room and board and a few dollars to send to México. That's all I need."

"I would leave there if I were you. Neither one of those two is worth the ground they stand on."

* * *

The paper tacked over the door said "STEUBEN RANCH." The eldest, Willie, was proud of that sign. It wore out every two months or so, but he would carefully stencil one out again, using the charcoal from the fireplace to fill in the spaces inside the block letters. It wasn't a large ranch, but it was all their German immigrant father had left them when the old man lay gasping on the metal bed and said, "Dieses land ist jetzt Euerland," and pointed out each of the three of them in turn. So Willie and Max had continued plowing the fields, and Ilse would store as much of the harvest as she could in the cellar. Having the *mojado* helped. They had let him stay in the small shack behind the barn, and Ilse would take his plate to the front porch or, if he happened to be in the barn, carry it out there. In the heat of the day, as she peeled and husked and cut and salted, and as the men worked the fields, she had sometimes caught glimpses of the tall brown body, with muscles that were lean and a chest that was smooth and hairless, unlike her older brothers', whose curly hair sprouted wildly from their arms and chests. But the glimpses were few, and work was the center of each of their days.

Still, summer ripened into fall, their interactions grew longer, and one day, when she'd gone with her brothers into town, she returned to find that the day's corn harvest had already been husked and restacked into the bushel baskets, and that one tray of the tomatoes looked suspiciously clean and moist. She glanced at the darkness of the shack and whispered something under her breath that not even she herself heard.

* * *

"I do not like it, José," said Daniel Ibarra, his hazel eyes shooting implications beyond his words. "Pedro's parents moved to México from here before the revolution, to help her sister. Now, the grey-haired *viejitos* try to come back, so that their son can take care of them, and some uniformed *oficiante* at the border tells them that they need papers. It's ridiculous! No one asked them for papers when they left here!"

José was silent, as he usually was when his knowledgeable friend shared news and *chisme*. Daniel remembered his young friend's short amount of leisure and asked, "Was there something you wanted me to send this time?"

"Yes, if it is convenient to you."

"Of course, of course."

"Sixteen dollars this time. Elsa talked them into raising my pay. She said they would lose me to other ranchers."

Daniel raised his eyebrows in question, but decided not to intrude on his friend's look of pride and pleasure, and simply accepted the worn bills, saying, "To your family, *¿como siempre?*" José nodded. Daniel noticed that the young man had begun to carry his shoulders straighter, and that his expressions were often filled with a vibrant color.

* * *

Ilse dished the food generously onto a plate and gathered a spoon, kitchen cloth, and her cloak before she headed out. She was small and thinner than she would have liked to be. Her father had always said it was a sign of a hard worker, and of purer blood, but still — she put on her cloak to cover the outline of her collar bones before going out to take the wetback his food. He stood when she entered the barn, and removed his hat.

"I hope it's still warm." He answered in his faltering English that the food was always good, and that she was very kind. She noticed as he smiled that the man had one tooth that gaped a bit to the side, and noted to herself that it was something like an extra smile behind his smile. That smile struck her as strangely attractive, and the peekaboo opening in it seemed to carry surprise and laughter.

She lingered. The sheriff was selling her brothers a horse, and it would take a while to work out a compromise. "That's a beautiful horse they're trying to buy. Have you seen it?"

He nodded, "I hold it for sheriff when he bring — yesterday."

"Even its hair shines," she said, trying to make use of any conversation possible.

"But not as much as yours," he thought, as he drank in her wheat-colored hair and her tightly drawn features. Somehow she heard his thought, and lowered her head, with a flush that added a special glow to her face. He lowered his head too, wanting to see more of this sunrise color to her face but scared that he might have transgressed to inpropriety in his stare.

"José." The way she said it caught him off guard, as if it were the Spanish phrase "Yo sé" ("I know"), but stopping just short of "Joséf." He realized it was his name and not the phrase, and liked the way the German "Y" lent a softness to the name. She must have realized how tender her voice sounded and, embarrassed, shifted to a pretense of efficient matronliness, asking if the shack was comfortable, and if there was anything he might need. "We have an extra blanket we never use — might it be of use to you?" His eyes softened in gratitude and searched hers again, as if for a moment he heard her thoughts. The laughter of the Steuben brothers and the slappy sound of pats on the back cut the air. "I'd better go now," she said, and left with just one look back, before exiting the barn door.

The next morning, she heard a soft knock on the door. José stood there, plate and spoon in hand, clean, and folded on top of them, the kitchen cloth she had brought him also washed and pressed by his hands into a neat square. No words passed, but he saw the sunrise growing on her cheeks again and turned quickly away, before her brothers could scold her for dallying.

As the weeks passed, his portions of food grew larger, the reasons she needed her brothers to go into town became more numerous, and José's English rapidly improved, though his moments of silence grew longer. She sometimes felt a bit guilty, as a person who has inappropriate thoughts feels guilty, but reassured herself that no indecency had ever been committed, for, after all, their time together included stares and words and smiles, but never had he so much as touched her hand. Still, she liked the way he pronounced her name

"Elsa," and noticed how the soft Spanish "s" gave a special beauty to her name.

One day, during another lingering trip to the barn to take him his supper, she forgot herself while he talked of the color of the ripened squash in their fields and the leaves that were already beginning to drop from the harvest-time plants, and allowed her eyes to rest on him undisturbed — watching the smooth outline of his dark body against the sun-bleached hay, and the dance of his black eyes in front of the kerosene lamp. Suddenly, he saw her thoughts again, but even knowing this, she forgot to lower her eyes. His words had finished and he, too, simply absorbed her, and it did not occur to him to lower his eyes. The moment stood free of time and free of everything except the absorption of this somehow peaceful joy.

"Ilse! Our glasses are empty! Hurry it up, will ya?!" Max's voice jarred them, and she left without glancing back. He went quietly to his shack, this time forgetting the plate of food behind him in the barn.

The next moment they had alone together, his jaw was set and sober, "I need . . . to say." She held her breath. Both of them knew some of what he was going to say, but neither knew how much , nor what she would reply. By the time Ilse left the barn she was dazed, but she somehow felt taller and more regal, and it did not occur to her to gather her cloak tightly around her neck, or to think of her collar bones, but instead, the fresh fall air blew freely against her skin above her dress, and she walked as if she, too, were free and light as the air. And as each week passed, she felt freer, lighter, taller.

*   *   *

She had not thought ahead. She had been too busy daydreaming and remembering to plan ahead what she would say. "No sister of ours is gonna marry a Mexican!" The sudden slap of their response was like being shook awake from a beautiful dream, and like the suddenly wakened, she was fierce and ill-tempered. Their shouts grew, the accusations and objections multiplying. Afterwards, she would be able to remember very little of it, but they would remember barely too much. At one moment, they even tried to convince her, Willie saying, "What folks in this town gonna think of you, if you livin' with a Mexican? What they gonna say about your children? Your children, they'd be Mexican, you know . . . What they gonna say of us?" and Max just ordering, "You ain't gonna do it, that's what!"

"I'm going to do what I want — you can like it or not like it, but you will not stop me!"

"You tie up with that greaser, and you not gonna get one piece of this land. This is Steuben Ranch, not Greaser Ranch."

"You can have your Steuben Ranch! I'll go to Mexico with him — and you can sit and worry about whether 'the greasers' are coming to take it away!"

"You couldn't! A greaser and a woman? Ha!" Max spit it out like a dirty joke.

In a moment, she was full of disgust. Ready to leave — the idea appealing to her more by the second. To leave behind her brothers — her brothers taking from her, demanding from her, expecting from her, waiting to be waited on. While José — well, José . . . and without warning it came out, "The two of you together don't make a tenth the man that 'greaser' is."

The brothers were speechless, pale. Riding on her anger, Ilse moved the chair out to the front porch, stepped up and pulled the paper sign from the door, ripped it and tossed it into the fire, saying, "Try to run this place without me! *You* wear the apron!" She tore her apron off, threw it at them, and went to her room, determined to continue her dream and her happiness.

Willie and Max had business in town the next day and had to leave the ranch. They left José at the farthest end of the ranch, fixing the fence alone, and said they'd pick him up on their way back that afternoon; that way, they felt sure that nothing would happen. He had wanted to take a jug of water with him, but they said the wagon was too heavy already, and there was a certain pleasure in Max's voice when he joked to Willie, "Maybe he'll die of thirst."

As they were getting near to town, a group of people on Parkerson's porch started laughing, and Willie looked over his shoulder nervously, wondering if they were laughing at them. They couldn't possibly know. And then, a little further along, some greasers were talking in Spanish and lowered their eyes as the Steubens passed — could they know? Were they secretly laughing at him too? Were they planning to move onto the ranch with all their family, like Mexicans do? Inside the store, Willie made a point to pronounce his English very carefully and to sound in every way like the storekeeper, whose grandfather had constructed most of the few buildings in the town. Max looked over his shoulder, too, whenever he heard a group talking low or laughing. They hurried home, and the ride was unusually hot and stifling, as Max fumed and Willie blushed, both feeling more like strangers in the town than they'd ever felt. Neither their arrival at their ranch nor the setting of the sun seemed to cool them.

At home, the food was on the stove, but Ilse had not served their plates. She came out of her room only once, and when Max sneered "Seen your greaser today?" She turned slowly and let it out like a cutting ice: "No, I haven't seen any men at all today. And I don't see any here now. Perhaps we could ask José to come in and help you run your ranch, since every ranch needs a *man*." Ilse poured her glass of water and went back to her room, as her brothers sat and silently boiled.

Something had to be done before people found out. Max was the one who thought of it really, but it kind of hatched on its own. They made their plans, almost without talking, almost without looking at each other eyes — they walked mechanically, simply, gathering what they needed. They were intoxicated on anger, yet when Willie closed the door behind them early that morning, he did it softly, partly not to wake Ilse, but more because he feared the slamming of the door might jar the two of them to wakefulness, a wakefulness they did not desire.

They arrived at the shack softly enough to hear his regular breathing. Then Max brought the plank down over his head, and Willie tied his arms. It was cold in the fields, and hard to carry the kicking wetback, who'd come to sooner than they'd hoped, but they wanted to run as quickly and quietly as possible. For all their anger, they did not want her to see. The wetback was making too much noise and fighting too hard, so they stopped short of their original destination, knocked him one to the jaw, threw the kerosene from the lamp towards his lean body, and lit the match.

Ilse woke with a start, some scream inside her jarring her sleep. Through the window she saw figures in the fields and heard the screams and with a sudden cold fear, tore through the door, past the shack, and out to that distant fire dancing in the fields. The blazing man ran on stumbling half-feet in one long tearing shout that would not stop. She arrived in time to see José running, ablaze, and then stop, his eyes on her, and fall to the ground, face forward, in silence. She ran to grab him but her brothers pulled her away. Ilse shook them off like poisonous vines and fell to the ground, taking up his long throaty scream and sobbing there till the sun finally came up.

*   *   *

The Méndez boys came in the morning to the Ibarra house, their trembling eyes almost scared to tell what they had seen and heard from a distance in the night, as they walked to town. They had gone to bring their tía, hoping she could help with the colicky baby, when they saw what they could hardly believe. Daniel was in shock. He could only absorb. Then he nodded, and they knew he would do something about it and left, feeling somehow protected. As Daniel turned, he saw his eldest daughter staring at him, eyes wide and face pale. Then she burst, ran to the bed, and cried and cried, something he realized he had not seen her do in three years.

Ibarra gathered his coat, closed the door quietly behind him, and started down the long road to town. He had always had better luck with the *gringos* than did his friends. Maybe it was because his lighter skin (*perlado*, his grandma had called him at birth) made it easier for them to see him as being like them — a little. Maybe it was his ability to read and write English — which many of the *gringos* could not — or to interpret the once-a-year correspondence they received in Spanish. He was sure the sheriff would listen.

*   *   *

Daniel stood, hat in hand, facing the sheriff. He had told all he knew, and the sheriff had averted his eyes. Finally, Mill looked at him and said, "What proof you got this happened?"

"We have the witnesses, sir, and the body — what's left of it should still be on the ranch."

"But how do I know this Ho-zay Silva exists? You got papers?"

"But he was a mojado, sir. You remember, he worked at the Steubens' place."

"I don't know of any illegals in this town . . . Need papers to show a man existed. Can't murder a man that never lived . . . You bring me the papers — 'til then, weren't no murder took place." And the sheriff stood up and adjusted his gun belt, a sign that the conversation was over.

At home, Dia was already dressing the straw doll for bed and covering him with his sheet, a crumpled paper she had found only today. Fifty years later, the story would still be told among the mexicanos of that place, in late-night whispers by the fire, and how the two brothers had died, one ten years later and one twelve, and how Elsa would sit in her night gown, blanket in her lap, rocking on her porch, year after year, staring out at the fields, as if she were looking at someone who didn't exist.

Federico y Elfiria

Pos, he liked her jus' 'cause of that — no le hacía — que era muy ranchera y nunca había visto más que su casa — She was a good girl, which is like saying that she wasn't a bad girl, not even a little bad, y'know?

The first time Federico started liking Elfiria was the day Chato and Manuel were teasing him and said that Frederico se vestía muy galán, that a lo mejor he was trying to impress the girls ... and then Manuel said that a lo mejor there was somebody he was already talking to a las escondiditas, and Chato (to impress Manuel) said he'd seen Elfiria writing notes with big hearts that said "Federico plus Elfiria." And they both laughed a lot at Federico, and Federico got red. He knew that a lo mejor Chato was just making it up but de todos modos, he wondered. I mean, it was real embarrassing. I mean, Elfiria was the kind of girl that didn't "like" nobody — she just went home from school and did what her parents said. And she wasn't the kind of girl that anyone went around "liking" either. I mean she was just somebody who sat in that desk and whose name got called two before his on the roll, and that's the only way anyone thought of her, y'know? But just the same, he wondered.

And I mean, she'd never had any boyfriends or anything, and you knew she was a good girl (which is to say, not a bad girl).

Well, the next day, Manuel and Chato were talking about the baseball game with Concho Mines High and wondering were they gonna lose now that Pato had joined the Air Force, and they had forgotten all about the love notes and the teasing. Federico remembered, but he wasn't gonna say anything. And then he started noticing how Elfiria always had her hair so neatly braided in a trenza, and none of the hairs ever loose, and it always fell right down the middle of her back, between her rounded shoulders. Well, he didn't know for certain if they were rounded, but he'd read something like that once, and they looked kind of round (como estaba ella media llenita, but that was okay, because everybody always made fun of guys that went with girls that were flacas and called them "Bone Chompers" and things like that. And I mean, nobody was gonna call her "La Gorda" of the class 'cause that was María de los Socorros, and there were lots of others almost as fat. Besides, good girls were supposed to be a little llenita so they wouldn't look like those mujeres in the movies who were definitely *not* good girls.

Still, he wondered. And once, when he was home alone and no one was lookin', he drew a little heart (in the corner of an old homework paper that he was going to throw away) and wrote "Federico + Elfiria" on it. And looked at it, just to see what it looked like (if she had done it, which she probably hadn't, 'cause she was a good girl), and he liked the way Elfiria had an F and an R in it, just like Federico. And he noticed how, when the teacher had them check each other's papers, she made her F's kinda nice and open, even when they were F's on somebody's paper. And then one day, Elfiria started looking at him. (Yeah, he looked at her lots, but he only did it when he was sure she didn't see, so it couldn't be that.)

Pues llegó summer. Y se casó Manuel. Y Chato se fue al Air Force, y en la boda de Polos, éste le dijo, "Ahora sólo quedas tú. You're the only one left, buddy." So he started going to Elfiria's house . . . y después de rato, se casaron.

About a year after they were married, he saw this movie. Not *dirty* dirty, tú sabes, but it had lotsa good parts in it. He came home all excited. Elfiria estaba lavando el piso, and he could see her nalgas pointing at him y también esas cosas hanging down. Pos, que se reventó el globo, and he was all over her. And him going for her and her fighting him off, kinda (in her feelings), but not saying "no" ('cause she was a good girl and s'posed to let her husband do things like that), and he was real excited, 'cause he knew that's what good girls were s'posed to do (but not do) if they were married. And he started kissing her lots, just kinda forgetting himself. And she even quit making faces for a while. And he was real excited and breathing on her neck hard, like when he — well, you know, did it — an' pos, they did, an' just when he was about to — well, you know, venir — he just grabbed her neck and kissed it with his teeth and tongue, sucking hard. I don't know why, maybe it was just seeing it in the movie that made him do it, but he didn't do it on purpose. And then he — pos estaba viniendo — and she could feel it, you could tell, and she did something that really surprised Federico — she grabbed his head in both her hands and kissed him real hard on the lips.

Well, they were both real sleepy after that and didn't think too much about it that night, but the next day, Federico was still turning this over in his head. I mean she'd never acted like that before. (He hadn't either, but then he'd seen this love movie, so that was why.) And then he started wondering if maybe she'd seen a movie, too, or something. I mean, she was supposed to be home during the day, and he hadn't heard nothing about her going out to movies. And this started to get his little hairs on his neck up and prickly until he realized she didn't have no way to get to no movie. And he relaxed.

But then Elfiria got up and started to get dressed, and when she took her robe off, the most horrible thing happened. Right in front of him there was this dark, dark blue mark on her neck and he *knew* what it looked like.

He'd seen those before (at school) but only on bad girls. It looked every bit like a hickey.

And I guess it was okay, what with his being her husband and all, but still — it looked funny and it bothered him. Manuel had always said, "Any girl that lets a guy give her a hickey is una d'esas." That night, Federico was still feeling bothered by it and, for some reason, didn't feel like going home right away. I mean he wasn't angry at her or anything, he said, he just wanted to stay out late. After all, he was a man, he could do that if he wanted. It was her business, cosa de viejas, staying home, and he went over to the cantina. He didn't go in, 'cause he didn't have but forty cents on him, and that was for a Coke to go with his taquitos tomorrow lunch, but he still went to the cantina, and he parked outside in the troquita his brother gave him, and he just watched from the dark. And when it was real late, he went home.

But she was still awake, and that pissed him off. And worse, she was looking at him nice-like, and like she wanted to do something. He just went around the bed, the other side, quitó los zapatos, and took his shirt and pants off quick, leaving his camiseta and underwear on, and slipped under the covers, facing the other way and looking asleep. She was in her gown and she curled up right against him. (¡Ingrata! So he could feel her!), and his heart was going double, but he didn't move a muscle, except for squeezing his eyes more shut to look more asleep.

Pos, if esa ingrata doesn't squeeze up against him even more, like hinting. And she stays like that, several seconds (or maybe hours), and he's so he can't take it any more and finally — all angry — he shoots off, "¡Cabrona! ¡Qué I'm asleep!" And she's so scared, 'cause he's never called her anything like that before, that she doesn't know whether to move away or how, and so she just stays absolutely still. And he's so mad that he had to speak that he keeps his eyes even more shut and his body even more still (so she can't say he's awake). And they stay that way the whole night — scrunched up against each other, his eyes squeezed shut, hers scared open, both of them scared to move an inch, and him with a hard-on and her hungry.

Bueno, that kind of did it. I mean, a man can only take so much, you know? I mean, a wife is s'posed to respect him, do what he wants when he wants, and not go bothering him otherwise, y'know?

And for the rest of that week, Federico went to the cantina every evening after work and stayed outside, parked in his troquita, and came home late and slept in his underwear. And Elfiria went to bed quietly, with her eyes open all night long.

Well, by the end of the week, they both looked pretty bad, but Federico looked the worst. Missing supper and not getting much sleep was really draining him. And Elfiria was lookin' okay, but pretty sad, and never said much — even more so than usual, and she usually didn't say much.

So one day, Federico thought, "Forget the cantina, I'm going home for supper." And Elfiria was so surprised, she ran around fixing supper as quick as she could, and they both ate, and without a word, he just went to the bedroom, pulled his clothes off (even his underwear — ¡ya le calaba!), and went to sleep. She did too. And they slept kinda comfortable. I don't know why, but maybe they were just too tired to care about the rest.

The next day was Saturday and things felt okay. I mean, really quiet, but they did the work they needed to do and then, come evening, ate and Federico went to bed early again. He lay and thought for a while, and wondered about that hickey of Elfiria's, but when she finished the dishes and came to lie down too, he noticed that it had faded almost away, and that made him feel better, so he drifted off to sleep.

Elfiria was really worried about Federico. I mean, she wanted to be a good wife, and she sure didn't like this business of him being angry, so she resolved to try not to do anything to upset him any more. Still, she thought about that one night lots, and how she had felt hot and shivery all over, and she tried not to think about it too much, but she fell asleep thinking about it anyway.

It was maybe 2:00 a.m. and they'd slept for several hours already, when suddenly Elfiria found herself dreaming half-awake and hungry and felt him hard and, just tired of waiting, she pushed herself against him and helped it along. And when Federico woke up, her hand was pushing his mouth against her neck and her — well, all the different parts of her were rubbing up against him, and it all felt real good for about twenty minutes, until he came. And then, he started realizing — well, he wasn't too certain what, but realizing it anyway.

An' he looked real quick to see if she had a hickey. And she didn't (or not that he could see in this light, anyway) and that made him feel a little better. But *still* . . .

And he fell asleep, but the next day he was worse upset than ever, and made her go to misa, while he stayed home and thought. Pos, then, if she doesn't up and hit him that week — right in the middle of all his confusion — con que she's pregnant. At first, Federico was even more confused — and irritated que la ingrata had gone and gotten herself that way right now, when he was trying to figure something else out. But then, when everybody found out, and all the guys patted him on the back and said que ya era tiempo, and Polos said his wife was expecting their second, and they all congratulated him, Federico felt pretty good. But still, he wondered. And the next day, he stayed away from work so he could watch the house from behind the bushes, to see if somebody else was coming to visit her.

The sun got pretty hot, y ya le andaban las moscas y el polvo, but he was determined to find out once and for all whether she was a good girl. Pos, if he didn't end up staying there hasta las 2:00 de la tarde, y lo único que vió was that Elfiria hung all his clothes on the line first, and then the toallas, and then her clothes. And then she gave the sobras al gato vecino. But most of the time, it was just him and the moscas, sufriendo del calor. At 2:00, he decided she wasn't gonna do anything more porque a esa hora she listened to her novela, and if she was going to do anything, she wouldn't have made it at that time, 'cause she'd miss "Amor de Lejos." So he decided it was his baby, and, relieved, he left, sin decirle nada.

He began to feel real good about her being pregnant, and as she got bigger each month, it made him feel more like uno de los hombres que eran middle-aged y bien-respected. Y ella se portó bien también, nomás que around her fifth month she started getting real wet and hungry at night, e ¡híjole! pregnant y todo, qué desgracia, pero what could he do? I mean, a man can only hold back so much, and there she was, *pushing* him to do it!

He didn't like the idea and he didn't agree with it at all — pero he was just too tired and turned on to fight it all the time. So, he'd go ahead and do it, and just agree with himself in the morning that it shouldn't be that way, you know, and that it wasn't his fault.

When the time came for him to take her to the hospital, she was screaming and all that woman kind of stuff. Federico tried to be strong for her, but then, as they were walking in the door, her water broke, y se mió allí, a chorros. "Elfa, can't you wait?!" le regañó in a whisper, embarrassed that the nurses should see his wife letting it all go like that. I guess Elfiria didn't hear him, 'cause she kept right on doing it, and her dress and the floor were all wet. And then he realized it had nothing to do with her going to the bathroom, and the nurse called for a wheelchair, and Federico's stomach felt funny (probably from the leftovers at supper last night), and he slumped onto the check-in counter with a color on his face Elfiria had never seen. For a second, Elfiria forgot her pains and just stared at him in shock, then she caught him just before he went to the floor, and pushed him into the wheelchair, saying to the nurse, "Cuídamelo."*

When he came to, she had already been taken in, behind those doors, and the nurse just smiled and said, "We'll let you know when you can go in."

Federico looked at the man in the wheelchair next to him, a viejito in his eighties, with an oxygen tube taped to his nose, who said to him, "Hijo, what are you in for?" It took Federico a few minutes to comprehend the question, but when he did, he scooted out of the wheelchair as fast as he could. Finally, they let him into Elfa's room, and it was real tough with her screaming and sweating and all, but Federico was real brave about the whole thing.

Sometime around midnight, the doctor came in to both of them, a yawning old man with a look como si había comido algo that didn't taste good, saw her still in labor, and said, half to the nurse and them and half to his clipboard, "Let's quit all this nonsense and get that baby out. I've got a golf game early tomorrow. She's been in labor five hours already — prep for a C-section." Federico was about to feel fear coming on when he was interrupted by this loud voice, strangely familiar, yet totally alien.

"¡NO SEÑOR!" It was Elfiria! Talking to the doctor like that! "If you won't help me, then go home and let my mother come!"

It was a boy. Named after him. Federico was in shock. He'd thought about her being pregnant, but he'd never really thought about the baby. Su hijo. Claro que era su hijo — he was named Federico Jr., wasn't he? And when he looked at him for the first time and saw this little person, all alive y pataleando, he just said, "I did that?!" and melted into a little pool of pride and tenderness.

Manuel had come pa' estar con él. "How ya doin', man? ¡Compa'! ¡Papá!" — and saw Federico's eyes water up as he answered, "God I feel...good." Manuel, smug over the birth of his own daughter two months earlier, smiled, muy compañero, and teased, "You feel good, huh? Oh, and it gets *better*, hombre. M'ija 'ta más chula . . . And you feel good now? Just wait till Elfiria gets all healed up and starts *wanting* you again — ¡uy!" He laughed and nudged Federico. Federico laughed, but only from the face out, porque what Manuel had said really bothered him. Y ni le dieron the time to absorb that when Elfiria was back in her room and ready for company . . .

Fred Jr. kept them both so busy that Federico didn't have much time to think about his earlier problems with Elfiria until one day, about seven weeks later, she comes up to him, real suavecito-like, y'know, and says, "Hace mucho tiempo. I'm healed now, tú sabes, down there . . ." Federico was touched, but,

---

* "Take care of him for me."

muy caballero, comforted, "That's okay, honey. I don't need it. I can wait some more." The dam burst, and Elfiria, tired and glad the baby was finally asleep, burst too. "But *I* need it! *I* can't wait some more!"

Federico was stunned. "But . . . you . . . ¡Hombre! . . . I always thought you were . . ." — he gulped and said it directly — "a good girl."

"¡Ya para con estas tonterías! Of course I'm a good girl! I'm more than that! Soy una madre — the mother of our *child* — y soy tu esposa — *wife,* you know. Like, *married?*"

Federico had never thought of it that way. He had always heard of — pos, tú sabes — *d'esas,* bad girls, y también of course de good girls — but of someone being a good girl plus more? Maybe that explained it. Maybe eso de ser mother and wife let her do these kinds of things *plus* be a good girl! He hadn't figured it out completely, pero Elfiria interrupted him and said, "¡Ya olvídate de esas cosas! Let's go to bed!" And they did, and pos, tú sabes, a man can only do so much all by himself.

Esa Casa Ya No Existe

"Me siento muy cansa'o," dijo el viejito barbón, y cerró los ojos pa' soñar otra vez.

"Tá loco," decía la hija, "Todavía habla de ir pa' su país. ¿Y cómo vas a ir? ¿A pié?"

"Ay, ya me voy pa' la casa, pa' ver a mis hermanas y los compañeros que viven allí por mi calle. Y ese cura condena'o que me regañó. Y pa' sentarme en la plaza por un rato."

Y la hija se reía, "¿No te acuerdas, viejo? Ya se murieron todas tus hermanas. ¿Y cúal calle? Hace setenta años que te fuiste. Esa casa ya no existe." Y se salió del cuarto para atender a su que hacer.

Y el viejito todavía murmurando, "Sí, me voy. Sí, me voy a ir. Pero ahorita no. Porque la vieja 'ta muy enfermita y no la puedo dejar al momento . . . ¿Vieja? . . . ¡Vieja, estás bien? . . . ¡Vieja, contesta!" Y el viejo comenzó a sentirse muy mal. Y el viejo se acordó . . . . . ."Pos, ahora si me voy. Ahora sí. Ya me voy. Ya me voy pa' mi casa."

Y la hija sacudía la cabeza, "No se le quita lo loco. Esa casa ya no existe." Y el viejito se quedaba con ganas de ir pa' su casa.

Un día el viejito paró de murmurar y de pelear. "Me siento muy cansa'o," dijo el viejito barbón, y cerró los ojos pa' soñar otra vez. Y soñando de su casa, se fue pa' su casa.

Pos, sí, la viejita enfermita ya se fue. Y el viejito barbón también se fue. Y hasta la hija mandona también se ha muerto. Y la casucha de mis abuelos se cayó.

Y a veces me siento cansada de trabajar y digo, "Ya me voy pa' la casa." Y me siento a pensar, y me acuerdo . . . que esa casa ya no existe.

Historia Sin Título

Una vez 'taba yo en el colegio y 'taba pero bien sura, man.

Me senté allí en la English class pa que me dijeran que yo no sabía ni escribir ni hablar ni pa eso, ni hasta escuchar. Y 'taba bien sura, man.

Y me decían que este writer 'taba mejor que ese writer porque el éste sí sabía como describir la gente como de veras eran — y me decían de su "realistic quality" y me preguntaban que "do you see that?" y yo que no veía nada. Y 'taba bien sura, man.

Y después nos ponían a write a theme, y que fuera un reaction al realism del libro. Y yo que decía que no veía nada en el libro, y que lo que era "real" era otra cosa. Pero me dijeron que el mundo verdadero y el basic reality se veía en ese libro, y que lo que yo había visto de la vida was unrealistic, unprofound, and not of the same universal quality de lo de ese writer (el safao).

Y por un momento cerré mis ojos y pensé.

Y ya entendí.

Que ellos ni sabían lo que 'taba pasando, porque they had learned it de los libros que had learned it de los libros que had learned it de los otros libros, y nadie sabía ni pensar.

Y ahora mi hermanita 'ta comenzando el junior college. Y le andan diciendo las mismas cosas. Y se viene después de class con la cara larga.

Y yo le digo que no se crea, pero ella dice que necesitamos "face reality" y que nosotros 'tamos bien tontos. Pero yo ya entendí.

Y se siente pero *bien sura*, man.

IV.
Selected Works For Children

Baby Coyote and the Old Woman

Baby Coyote saw the desert. He liked his desert. Its air was clean and its skies were many colors. He liked to run in the open spaces, chasing tumbleweeds. He liked to watch the cactus flowers bloom and the horned toads scamper across the dust. But what he liked to watch most was the old woman. Baby Coyote saw the old woman come out of her back door every morning, when the sun was just peeking up over the desert. He saw her water her garden. He saw her leave him a cool delicious drink of water in the old pot under the faucet. The old woman did not see Baby Coyote, but every morning she saw his tracks. She knew he was a very tiny baby coyote, so every night she would leave a few scraps by her back door. And every night, in return, Baby Coyote would chase the rabbits and the prairie dogs away from her garden.

Every day, the old woman would grind her corn. Then she would either nail or paint or sweep or hoe. And before the sun had traveled across the sky, there would be the delicious smell of tamales or soup or tortillas or some other good smell floating out of her back door. Baby Coyote liked the smells from the old woman's house, and he liked even better the taste of the scraps the old woman would leave for him.

But scraps were not the only thing the old woman put out at night. She would also take her trash and throw it in a big pile behind her house. Baby Coyote liked the old woman, but he did not like the trash pile. Sometimes the desert wind would blow, and the pieces of paper from the trash would blow across the desert and catch on the cactus plants, hiding the pretty cactus flowers. Sometimes the tin cans would catch the bright hot light of the noonday sun and hurt Baby Coyote's eyes. And once, an almost-empty bottle of cleaner spilled a few drops of its poison in a little circle on the ground. And the next day, Baby Coyote found the baby cactus flower wilted and the baby cactus plant dead.

One night, Baby Coyote picked up a piece of the paper in his baby mouth and carried it to the old woman's door. The next morning, the old woman picked it up and said, "Well, maybe I can use this paper to help light my stove."

The sun went up and the sun went down, and the next day, the old woman found a whole *pile* of papers in front of her door. "Oh, my!" she gasped. "Well, I guess I can take these to town on my Saturday trip, to the place where they gather papers."

That night, Baby Coyote picked up a tin can in his baby mouth and carried it to the old woman's door. The next morning the old woman picked it up and said, "Well, maybe I can use this can to hold my seeds."

The sun went up and the sun went down, and the next day, the old woman found a whole *pile* of cans in front of her door. "Oh, my!" she gasped. "Well, I guess I can take these to town on my Saturday trip, to the place where they gather papers and cans."

That night, Baby Coyote very, very carefully picked up something in his baby mouth and carried it to the old woman's door. The next morning the old woman found an almost-empty bottle of cleaner in front of her door. Then she saw the little tracks of the tiny baby coyote, leading away from her doorstep, and she sat down on her doorstep to think.

She thought all day, and she thought all night, and finally, Baby Coyote, who was thinking too, came to sit with her, just a little distance away. When she saw that beautiful baby coyote, she knew what she had to do.

The next day, the old woman made three stacks in her tool shed. One was paper, one was metal, and one was glass and plastic. And on Saturday, she took them to town.

"What will happen to these things?" she asked the man at the gathering center. "The papers will be recycled, to make new paper," said the man, "and the metal will be melted down and recycled to make new metal." "What is recycled?" said the woman. "Oh, that is when an item can be used again, and go through another cycle, like having another life." "Like when the sun comes up again for another day?" said the woman. "Yes, exactly," said the man.

"But what about the bottles?" asked the woman. "Oh, that is harder," he said. "All of the glass bottles can be reused, but some of the plastic bottles have had dangerous chemicals in them. Some things can never be used again, and they never go away." "Then we must not use those things," said the woman, "or we must use less, and throw away less."

The next week, the old woman sat on her back doorstep, and looked out over her desert. And Baby Coyote looked out over his desert. Its air was clean and its skies were many colors. There were open spaces and horned toads and pretty cactus flowers. And both Baby Coyote and the Old Woman liked what they saw.

Mari and the Moon

Mari and the moon
are the best of friends.
One reaches up and stretches,
one reaches down and bends.

One points and calls her name out,
the other sends her light.
One rides her Daddy's shoulders,
the other rides the night.

One sings and laughs and giggles.
one dances with a cloud.
One learns a new word every day,
one is so old she's proud.

One sits upon a horsie,
toes dangling, dreaming meadows.
One sits perched on a rooftop,
toes playing with the shadows.

One peeks out through the window
to see her friend in sky.
One sneaks her fingers through curtains and cracks,
her touch — a lullaby.

Mari and the moon
are the best of friends.
They play together every night:
one sleeps, and one pretends.

The Discovery

Let's get our history straight now!
America discovered Columbus
while he was lost upon a beach
and wondering, "Whaddagumbus?"

Some sunbronzed women working there
said, "Who's that crazy fellow?
And why's he got his lips on the ground
and his rear end up to yell, 'Oh —

I've found it! Yes, I've found it!
It's India for sure —
God bless this Land — and Lordy —
it's for seasickness the cure!'
And why does he keep staring
at our bodies strong and clean
when he is dressed so strangely
and his B.O.'s rather mean."

The word spread fast throughout the land:
some weirdos had arrived.
And when some heard their skin was steel,
they knew it was contrived.

Then someone's Gramma said, "Don't be
so rude to these poor folks!
When company arrives, you give
them gifts and food and cloaks!"

So off they went to pass around
the hat and get donations,
While Gramma called the Emperor
to invite the League of Nations.

They gathered plumes of rarest birds,
and got the banquet ready,
and added trinkets for the wrapping:
Gold — useless, yes, but pretty.

Onto the roads came the Americans.
Said the lost, weary sailor, "Hello, Indians.
Could you lead me now to Bombay?"
(Some began to have their opinions . . . .)

Let's get our history straight now!
America discovered Columbus
while he was lost upon a beach
and wondering, "Whaddagumbus?"

Las Gotitas Presumidas

Los gotitas moradas
y las gotas color gris
se decían, presumidas,
y muy monas, entre sí:

"Nosotras no nos vemos
tan común ni tan feítas
como las gotas amarillas
ni las gotas cafecitas.

Ya juremos entre nosotras
que para hoy en adelante,
no les hablaremos
ni si el mero sol nos cante."

Pues la madre nube, triste,
se puso a llorar
y esa gorda comenzó
sus lagrimas a echar.

Y con la lluvia fuerte,
nuevos ríos se formaban
donde gotas cafecitas
con las grises se mezclaban.

Y el jugo del limón
se mezclaba con el vino,
y la madre nube, viendo
sus hijos juntos, dijo:

"Ya verás, mis gotitas,
que no hay que presumir,
si todos vivos tienen
sus razones de vivir,

Si todos tienen gracia,
y cada uno su belleza,
su talento, su lucir,
su valor y su rareza.

Y sin todos los colores
en el mundo y en las vidas,
no hubiera arco iris,
sino solo aburridas."

Y por eso ya las gotas
se mezclan en el cielo;
después de cada lluvia
arco iris es su anhelo.

Tacho, el Baby Tacuache

Once upon a time, there was a Baby Tacuache named Tacho. Tacho was born with twenty-three brothers and sisters, and they all lived inside their mother's pouch. It was warm and quiet inside their mother's pouch, and she took very good care of her little tacuachitos because she loved them very much. She gave them food, she sang them songs, she took them out for walks, and she taught them many things. One day, when Tacho was out for a walk, she gave him a crayon and a piece of paper, and she taught him how to draw.

Tacho loved to draw. And he loved to draw *big*! He drew big houses and big trees and giant flowers and lots of stars in a big sky. He drew apples and chairs and bottles and beans (big beans, of course). He drew and drew and drew until he was very tired. Then Mama put him in her pouch again so he could take a nap, for he was a very tiny tacuachito. While he was asleep, he dreamed that he was drawing everything he saw, and it was very, very beautiful.

When Tacho woke up, he felt so good that he wanted to jump out of the pouch, get another piece of paper, and draw some more big wonderful things. But his twenty-three brothers and sisters were still asleep, and he did not want to wake them up, so he sat very still and looked at his drawings. He waited and waited and waited, but his brothers and sisters still had not awakened. Then, he got an idea. He looked up at the wall of his mother's pouch, and he looked at his crayon, and he thought, "I'll surprise Mama! I'll draw a beautiful big mesquite tree on the wall of her pouch!" So he sat very quietly and drew a large mesquite tree. But the wall began to shake. Mama began to shake. The pouch began to shake. And of course, Tacho and all his brothers and sisters began to shake, too. They started to wake up. Some began to cry and some began to shout. Some were scared because their warm, safe pouch was shaking, and some were angry because they had been woken up.

Mama said, "Ay, Dios mío ¿qué pasa? Everyone is crying. What is happening?" And she looked inside her pouch and saw. "Oh, my goodness! There's a mesquite tree in there! How did a mesquite tree get in my pouch? No wonder my stomach felt like shaking!" Tacho shouted, "No, Mama, that's not a real mesquite tree. That's my drawing! I drew a mesquite tree, Mama!"

"Ay, Tacho!" said Mama Tacuache, "You must learn. Don't draw on the walls! Draw on paper, draw on canvas, but *please* — don't draw on the walls!" Tacho was very sorry he had woken everybody up, and he promised he would never again draw on the walls of Mama's pouch. But he still loved to draw. And he loved to draw *big*!

After Tacho and his twenty-three brothers and sisters got too big for the pouch (and believe me — with twenty-three brothers and sisters, things can get *very* crowded) Papa and Mama Tacuache built them a house. The house had so many beautiful green plants all around that it almost looked like a jungle. There was only one thing missing, thought Tacho — a lion. So one day, he drew a big beautiful lion on the walls of the Tacuache Home. He thought it was great! When his brothers and sisters got home and saw the lion, they shouted, "Dios mío, it's a lion!" and ran screaming out of the house. Tacho thought that was funny, but Mama and Papa Tacuache did not think it was funny at all. Papa Tacuache said, "Ay, Tacho! You must learn! Don't draw on the walls! Draw on paper, draw on canvas, but *please* — don't draw on the walls!" Tacho said he would try to remember, and he promised he would*never* draw on the walls of their house again. But he still loved to draw. And he loved to draw *big*!

Soon, Tacho was big enough to go to school. There were many things at school — books and desks and blackboards and a big white wall on one side of the room. The teacher asked all the tacuachitos to draw a mouse and an elephant on their paper. Tacho drew very carefully — a big, beautiful mouse. You've never *seen* such a healthy ratón! But then he realized he didn't have any room left on his paper for the elephant. "Y ahora qué?" he thought. Then he saw the big beautiful white wall, and quick as a flash, he filled it with the most wonderful life-size elephant. And it wasn't just *any* old elefante — era una elefantota! Pretty soon, all his classmates were running over to pet the elephant, and trying to climb up on the elephant, and throwing peanuts at the elephant — and pretty soon, the classroom began to look like a zoo. And Tacho's teacher got very, *very* mad. He said, "Ay, Tacho! You must learn! Don't draw on the walls! Draw on paper, draw on canvas, but*please* — don't draw on the walls!" Tacho remembered having heard that somewhere before — but he had thought it was only pouches' walls and houses' walls he should avoid. And he sighed and guessed that schools' walls, too, were to be avoided. Tacho felt very sad. He *loved* to draw. And he loved to draw *big*.

Every day on his way to school, he would dream about drawing — drawing big beautiful pictures that everyone could see a mile away! And every day, on his way to school and back, he would pass this big blue wall. And it was a*big* blue wall. He would think about how much it looked like the big blue sky on a sunny day — and he would think about how it was only missing a few things to make it a big wonderful sky. It was missing some fat white clouds and a big bright sun and some tree branches reaching up to touch it, and birds sitting in the tree branches, and a kite that was flying high at the end of a string held by a girl running in a big park, and an organ-grinder with a monkey, and a raspa-vendor, and some babies playing with balloons, and...

Oh, it would make such a beautiful big sky. But he sighed, and remembered someone saying to him once (or maybe twice) . . . (or maybe three times) . . "Don't draw on the walls!" So he didn't. But he looked at it every day.

One day, Tacho was walking past that beautiful wall and thinking*very* clear thoughts, when he heard someone say, "Oh, that wall just looks so empty!" He turned around quickly, chasing his tail and asking himself, "Did I say that? I didn't *think* I said that."

"No, *I* said that!" said Señora Sonrisa. She was a friendly woman with a beautiful big smile, so everyone called her "Señora Sonrisa" (which means Mrs. Smile.) Tacho liked Señora Sonrisa very much. He said, "Oh, please don't be sad, Señora Sonrisa — everyone would miss your smile!" And she said,

"But every morning, I walk up to my store, and all I see is a big blue wall, and it seems so . . . ."

"Empty?" said Tacho, and he was already smiling with a big delicious idea! So, he and Señora Sonrisa had a long talk, and the next day . . . as people were driving home from work, and tacuachitos were walking home from school, and kitty cats were looking for ratones, they all stopped!

. . . and looked at the most beautiful big blue sky with fat white clouds and a big bright sun and some tree branches reaching up to touch it, and birds sitting in the tree branches, and a kite that was flying high at the end of a string held by a girl running in a big park, and an organ-grinder with a monkey, and a raspa-vendor, and some babies playing with balloons, and he had even added a life-size picture of Señora Sonrisa with a big smile in front of her store (which most times looked like you were seeing double, because most times Señora Sonrisa *herself* was standing with a big smile, in front of her store, looking up at that sky, *just* like in the picture!) And off in a corner, under some big green plants, were Mama and Papa Tacuache and twenty-three little tacuachitos, and off in the farthest corner of the corner, the tiniest tacuachito of all — Tacho!

Well, many years passed by, and Tacho, el Baby Tacuache, became known first as Mr. Tacuache, then Mr. Tacuachote, and finally, respectfully, Don Tacho. He still loves to draw, and he still loves to draw *big*. But now, people pay him to draw on their walls — big lovely paintings with lots of bright colors, just the way Tacho likes them.

And sometimes, people ask him, "Sir? Don Tacho? Could you tell us how you became such a wonderful Muralist and World-Renowned Artist?" and Tacho (that is, Don Tacho) answers from behind his now-grey whiskers, "By learning to *never* draw on walls!"

However, the last time we saw Tacho, he was staring at a BIG, BIG, big empty wall, on the side of the Grand Canyon . . . .

V.
Autobiographical Notes

Autobiographical Notes

Carmen Tafolla

I know when I began — or at least when I was born, on July 29th, 1951, at 8:41 p.m. — but that isn't really the whole story. My beginnings were somehow rooted in memories passed on to me through my grandmother's sayings and my father's songs, and my mother's stories, and in some mountains that I saw once from the highway, and in the thread of a dream below the voice and between the words of someone whose name I don't know but whose voice and dream I still carry.

When did I start writing? many ask me, and (strangest of all) where did I learn to write? I don't have the answers for these, either. I know that my mother always carried a pen, even if it was only to take problems to paper and then tear the paper up. I know that I watched my father and mother both study The Book and turn pages for answers, as they prayed, and that I, too, learned to follow along and turn pages and follow words. But the memories that are even more vivid are of Saturday evenings "visitando." People were our major recreation, also our major work, pastime, expression, responsibility, enjoyment, meaning, and definition. "En el rancho" outside Martín's *gasolinera*, surrounded by the sound of coyotes and crickets, or in the parlor "de mis tías," with the sounds of hotrodded Chevies and barrio paleta wagons going past, the major activity of my early life was centered on language — the telling of stories, the sharing of "qué le pasó" of family and friends, the preaching of "cómo portarse como la gente" and "cómo ser respetuoso a Dios y a nuestro hermano."

Words always fascinated me — and always seemed both familial and alien (pero con respeto). There was always the inside-outside of being in a world where the "other world" existed — where Spanish was a perspective on English and English was a perspective on Spanish. There were two constant codes which life followed, and we lived someplace on the patchwork created by them both. The written word was just a subsection of the entire world of words, many of the most powerful of which we never saw in writing. So when I speak of writing, my *own* writing, I speak of the pattern of words that make a story or create a vision, or paint a person, or a world, and that pattern arises out of a context that may or may not fit on the printed page. Writing as Oral Writing, as Story-telling, as Language Magic, which is then sometimes documented with pen and paper.

I cannot deny that there was an urge to write — to explore the origins and faces of words, to tell the story behind things, people, sayings — why this constant urge to tell the story, to explain, to bring closer together the understanding, the relationships between beings, things, places? The scenes of the storytelling blend together — the hot front porch of a San Antonio barrio summer night and the kerosene lantern on the dirt floor of an adobe casita in the night-cold mountains of México — all seem the same moment and the same place. The telling of the stories seemed to be in my veins and in the pattern of my mind.

It wasn't that I always thought I would be a writer. Quite the opposite, I never thought that "being a writer" was truly attainable. Writers came from New York, or traveled the world, or saw Rome, or were somehow from that other alien world. It's just that I never recognized that what we were doing, every "visita" or Saturday night or Sunday afternoon or mealtime, was the birthmother of writing. I was fascinated by writing, but as a poor kid in a toy store whose items he is delighted to simply be allowed to see, not touch, I never dreamed that it would be within my reach. It was a luxury, one my mechanic father and housewife mother were denied along with the niceties of formal higher education. Still, it fascinated me, and when other kids asked their parents if they could go to the "Toy" aisle of the grocery store to look, while parents worked industriously on comparing prices of beans or fideo, I asked my parents if I could go the paper aisle, and stare at little notebooks that came with their own miniature ruled notebook paper. It was wonderful.

Mi Familia

The way I defined family was much like the old funerals I remember. In the front rows were the next of kin, the most greatly affected by the loss, behind them those close, behind them the friends, then the acquaintances, and always, somewhere, the people of whom no one knew the exact relationship to the departed, but that didn't matter — these people knew, and that was enough reason to be there. In fact, one's own internal reasons were the guiding law for anyone's presence, and no one had to make explanations at a time like that. Modern "family sections" later served to cut off, to make people separate off who was family from who wasn't, who was "immediate family" from who was "distant." None of this was necessary in the old mexicano funerals I remembered. The cousin ("prima hermana," to emphasize how close the relationship really was) who'd spent eighty years of her life with the deceased didn't have to be turned away from the three skimpy rows of "Family Section" just in order to allow room for younger siblings and spouses, nieces and nephews, who'd only spent twenty to sixty-some-odd years with the deceased. There was no having to judge "degree" of relationship, in competition with the others present. One merely found one's place according to one's own intuition.

Family was like that. There was the little boy in second grade that I was proud to claim as my "third step cousin-in-law" and there were the friends for whom no blood connection existed, but who counted in every way as cousins, to whom there was a life-long commitment and a life-long connection.

It was a big family. It seemed I had several dozen aunts and uncles, and at least fifty of the immediate cousins. It was a context that provided variety and contrast. "Somos como los frijoles pintos," my grandmother would say, "algunos güeros, algunos morenos, y algunos con pecas." I knew my grandmother so

Tafolla's grandparents, Mariano F. Tafolla and Eloisa Sanchez de Tafolla, with their children, left to right, back row, Eloisa, Fidel, Esther, Sofia, Annie, Sara, Margie, Febe, front row, Lina, Nano (Mariano), and Bobby. "My grandmother spoke little and said much. . . . My grandfather . . . was a man who valued tools."

Tafolla's father, left, with brother and sisters. "My father would later teach me . . . how to hunger to build things."

Tafolla's grandmother, Eloisa Sanchez de Tafolla, with youngest sons, Mariano, left, and Bobby, right. "I knew my grandmother so well . . . through my father."

well, through all her sayings, but these had been told to me by my father, years after her death. I knew her through my father, even the details of her death, a death that happened shortly after my first birthday. Still, she guides me through many days, telling me "No hay sábado sin sol ni domingo sin misa," warning me "Díme con quien andas y te diré quien eres."

She was from Mexico, a proud, quiet woman, who spoke little and said much, whose skirts always touched the ground, who never raised her voice or lowered her sense of dignity. Her high cheekbones were echoed in my father's face and in my own. I find it hard to imagine her as a noisy child, as a noisy anything.

My grandfather, on the other hand, lived by words, words were his tools, and he was a man who valued tools. "Cómprate un fierro con cada día de pago," he gave my father as consejo, and he taught his sons carpentry, plumbing, construction, and a hunger to build things. My father would later teach me, perhaps more randomly than he would have constructed the lessons for a boy, but still I knew how to use a hammer and a drill, how to putty the nail holes and clean a carburetor, and most importantly, how to hunger to build things. Had the training been less random, less riddled with gaps, I would have known *how* to build things. As it is, I sit with pen and paper today, and try to plan and guess how I could put together a table or a house, how to do it right, for it would not do to make one not solid, not *"macizo."*

Yet my grandfather's main occupation in life was using words as tools. The preacher, teacher, leader, he was the first in the family (possibly in the whole barrio) to own a typewriter. I don't know how old he was when he got it, but it was still his, marked with his work and his determination, used solidly and squarely as any of his tools, the fountain of many letters, that somehow always looked as individual as if he'd marked them by fountainpen and fingerprint.

His name was Mariano Tafolla. It was his grandfather's name, my father's name, and my father's oldest brother's name. Searching through the Santa Fe archives a few years ago, I found his grandfather's signature. It was almost a duplicate of my father's. I keep the name Tafolla, although my signature, perhaps even my personality, are far different. Perhaps it has something to do with words. With finding your place in the old mexicano funerals, by internal guide, by intuition. This is who I am.

My roots in New Mexico go back for centuries —*españoles* arriving in the 17th century to *indio* parientes already there. The move to Texas happened between 1848 and 1865 (a few wars got in the way, caused strange demographic reshuffles). My great-great-grandmother had a seamstress shop in "downtown" San Antonio; my great-grandmother washed clothes in the San Antonio River; her *tío* had brought word in 1836 to Juan Seguín and the tejanos at the Alamo that Santa Ana's army was coming in great force. They didn't listen. She later married two (one at a time) Confederate veterans. Growing up, I teased that I had relatives on all sides of all wars.

The Tafollas' roots were in New Mexico, the Salinas' in San Antonio, the Sanchez' in Montemorelos, the Duartes' and Morenos' in Spain, but somehow it was San Antonio that won out. San Antonio is in my blood. From the vaqueros, rancheros, soldados, preachers, teachers, and storytellers on my father's side and the metalworkers, maids, nursemaids, and servantpeople on my mother's side come the family members that sit by my side as I write today. So do the mesquite trees and *vacas*, *coyotes* and *ríos* of their lives, and the *molcajetes* and *gatos*, *libros* and computers, friends and strangers, races, telephones and headlines — of mine.

Mi Barrio

I have always considered my life one of great fortune, and the barrio was one of these points of fortune. It was a place rich in story and magic, warmth and wisdom. So magic it was that even the police would not come there, despite calls or complaints, unless they came in twos, with their car doors locked. We played baseball in the streets, shot off firecrackers on the Fourth of July, raised our Easter chicks to fully-grown (and temporarily spoiled) chickens, and dialed La Llorona's phone number on scary nights to hear her cry "A-a-a-ay, mis h-i-i-i-ijos."

When I was, years later, to hear about slums, and ghettos, cultural deprivation, and poverty-warped childhoods — there was no identification in my mind with these. In our own view, we were wealthy — we had no deprivation of cultural experiences, but rather a double dose of *cultura*. Yes, my cousins from "up north" would come to visit, and they had so many more "facts" at hand, seemed to know so much and do so much in their schools. Our school had no interscholastic activities, no spelling bees or science fairs, no playground equipment nor even a fence. I was always caught in silent observation when they began to discuss school.

But then this was the essence of being an observer twice, a resident of two worlds. There was our world, and there was the other — that other world typified by Leave It to Beaver and Roy Rogers, by Mouseketeers, and Tom, Betty and Susan. In adaptation of Tevye, "We didn't bother them, and — so far — they hadn't bothered us." This was the world of *pilón*, the unexpected surprise, the irrelevant-to-legal (and sometimes illegal) extra — non-required, non-charged, non-assessed. This was the world where one lucky Sunday morning out of twenty, you would be awakened at the crack of dawn to share the family ritual of *barbacoa*, and *bolillos*, those crusty white French breads that ironically shared the name we called those "others" of the TV world and the world of officialdom. And on another early Sunday morning, you would be awakened by the La Llorona-like screams of the police siren. This world rich with sensation would accost you, shape you, train you, with the permanent warmth of the smell of flour tortillas, and then sharpen you, remind you, with the acrid piercing odor from *las matanzas*.

It was not until I was an adult professional, driving through the streets of another town, that I realized that my greatest fear of driving in "strange areas" was triggered not in the barrio or inner-city streets, not in the poor neighborhoods of any town, where the houses were close together, and the people always spilling out, hanging out, overflowed, overlapped, but in those strange and alien Leave-It-to-Beaver-type suburbs, houses far from the strreet, far from each other, inaccessible and strictly manicured, controlled and straight and so uniform they seemed bare. If my car were to break down there, who would there be to help? If I were to get lost, how could I possibly tell one block from the next? If I were in trouble, who would even know?

Las Escuelas

Had I know how central school and schooling was going to be to my life perhaps I would not have walked out on the first day. Then again, had I known then what I know now, perhaps I would have walked out more purposefully, more in principle, and more permanently. It's strange to consider what a forty-year-old would do in a six-year-old's situation.

But I neither suspected nor pondered on that first day of school at Ivanhoe Elementary, a day I had eagerly awaited, rising for three successive days to dress in a dress (not my customary T-shirt and corduroy pants), gather my crayons and tablet, and wake my sleeping parents with my "terca" question, "Is it time to go to school?" When the day finally arrived, and the event finally happened, I sat quietly in my chair for an hour or so, observing the strange chaos, then rose and walked out of the classroom, saying, when stopped, "Thank you for school. I'm going home now."

School became a central point for learning — but the major curiculum was recess, and the main subject matter was behavior. The main thing the schools tried to teach us was not to speak Spanish. The main thing we learned was not to speak Spanish in front of the teachers, and not to lose Spanish within ourselves. Perhaps that is why so many good independent and critical minds came out of that time period. Or perhaps that is why so many good independent and critical minds dropped out of school. We learned — oh, did we learn, but it was not what the school district had planned for us to learn. It was much bigger than that.

We became filled with a hunger — I call it now, sometimes, Latino Hunger. A hunger to see ourselves, our families and friends, our values and lives and realities reflected in something other than our own minds. We wanted proof that we really existed — a proof documented in those many schoolbooks filled with Tom-Betty-and-Susan's and Dick-and-Jane's, but no Chuys or Guadalupes or Juanas, no Adelitas or Santos or Esperanzas. And we definitely needed Esperanzas if we were to dream anything at all beyond the sirens, the friskings, and the punishments for the sin of having spoken Spanish at school. There was a hunger and a place in our lives that needed to be filled with Esperanzas and Milagros.

So what we didn't see, we invented. Even the national anthem became our cultural playground: "Jo-o-sé, can you see-ee?" And we filled TV with our own raza, hidden between the lines and in the shadows of people's pasts. In my family, we said that Lloyd Nolan was really Moses Tafolla, who had left for California many years before and never been heard of again till he surfaced in a Hollywood movie as Lloyd Nolan, but looking every bit like his brother Federico Tafolla. Young, short, dark-haired Chicano guys later spread the rumor that young, short, dark-haired "Baretta" was really a Chicano. To this day, we watch the credits on films, noting Duráns and Armijos and Martínezes, and wondering if Moran was really Morán. Had the teachers known at the time that our hunger was so extreme, I wonder, would they have filled it, or made it even more prohibited?

The neglect with which they treated us in elementary (with the exception of one sixth-grade teacher who made of our classroom a Time Machine and a Travel Tour, a Dream Fountain and a Spirit Saver) was followed by the fear and apprehension with which they treated us in junior high. Daily friskings, purse checks, and homeroom lectures drilled us constantly on their view of us. Teachers' expectations of us as a whole were so low that at one point the junior high principal "complimented" me by telling me I had potential to make it "all the way to high school." There were only two non-Mexican-Americans in the school — an Anglo daughter of a missionary who'd come "to serve the Mexican people" and a Chinese-American boy who was considered the smartest boy in the school. The Anglo girl had been in the "C" class on the white side of town, and since we were constantly told that "an A here is only worth a C at Alamo Heights," she was put in the "A" class here, my homeroom. She made C's, her father tired of the Mexican people after one semester, and she moved. As for Rodney, the Chinese boy, the teachers continued to feed his self-image as the "smartest kid in school" and the rest of us looked on, while listening to lectures urging the boys to give up their switchblades and the girls to refrain from carrying mirrors and perfume bottles, and to neither let their hair grow too long nor to tease it. ("Why?" we foolishly asked. "Because if you get into a fight, you'll break the mirror and slash at somebody with it, or pull the switchblade out of your teased hair," they explained. And, tragically, we continued to learn a lot at school.)

In eighth grade, I was asked to go take a scholarship test at some place on what my parents and I considered the far north side of town. The teachers excitedly explained that Rodney had taken the test last year while in eighth grade and gotten a half scholarship, but had turned it down hoping to try again in this second year for a full scholarship. They had even asked Rodney to come give me some helpful pointers (although Rodney told me that I, a mere eighth-grader, a girl, and not a genius like he, didn't stand much of a chance). I didn't understand what scholarships (which I had always assumed were for college) had to do with junior high students, but I followed orders and went to the private school's testing session, along with four representatives from each junior high in town. Three weeks later, after testing and finalist testing, I was called to the office and told that Rodney and I had each earned a full scholarship to Keystone, a private academically-accelerated high school. I was told to call my parents and give them the "good news." Rodney was already on the phone, but condescended "Go ahead. My line is busy anyway." The principal and counselor were ecstatic; I was neither elated nor comfortable. I picked up the phone and dialed the only phone number I knew. The principal never guessed that my parents had no phone, and I nervously carried on a whispered conversation in the middle of the office, speaking in a forbidden Spanish to an elderly aunt who couldn't figure out why I was calling her in the middle of a schoolday. "If my parents go by there today, tell them I got a scholarship." "Are they coming by here today?" "No, but if they do go by, tell them I got a scholarship." "A what?!!"

I am still surprised that I ended up going to that private school — neither I nor my parents were pushing for it. Only the teachers at the school spoke as if this were some kind of incredible salvation. And somehow, both Rodney and I ended up attending the school, he in pride, I in homesickness for my barrio school. The first year there was a difficult one — not academically, but socially. It was a year of culture shock — not because there were no Hispanics — there were a few at each grade level — but because these were not from the barrio or the culture I knew, but instead, children of doctors and lawyers, and their upbringing seemed as strange to me as that of the middle and upper class "white" kids. Ironically, my own color further educated me. My classmates would tell me how "You can't walk through the West Side — you'll get stabbed," never suspecting that every day I would walk home from that school and two buses, through the West Side and through my beloved barrio.

But the adaptations were made, and the exposure to the academic world proved an advantage. My classmates went on to "Name" colleges; I didn't even apply to those, scared of the cost, but chose a college that had given me enough scholarships, loans, and grants to allow my work-study check and my parents' small supplements to pay the bill. I would sign the check receipt for scholarship and loan money at one window and sign the same check back over to the college at the next window. After two semesters on the Dean's List, the Dean asked me to babysit for his kids, and I jumped at the chance. In keeping with my childhood's taste, I usually spent this only discretionary money at the bookstore, on empty notebooks and special stationery, non-required books, or an occasional foreign language dictionary.

A Bachelors and a Masters were all I could imagine, and I completed them in 1972 and 1973. When I first joined the faculty of a small college, as Director of their Mexican American Studies Center, and other faculty began to ask me if I planned on completing a doctorate, I would react emphatically, "No!" Three years on the faculty side of higher ed's desk began to soften me to the idea. A summer of graduate school at the University of Texas convinced me it was possible. I decided to get a Ph.D, "aunque tenga que vender tacos para hacerlo." I looked around at several possible areas of study. My final decision would not have surprised those classmates who suffered through the years of "No Spanish" rules with me: Bilingual Education.

Los Trabajos

"El trabajo bien hecho es un placer," my grandmother would say, and "El que nace para tamal, hasta del cielo le caen las hojas." Pues me cayeron muchas hojas, y cada una de un sabor distinto. The summer between my B.A. and M.A. found me desperate for employment. I was told my chances were slim because I didn't type and had no experience as a waitress. After three weeks of job searching, I found a Denny's manager who would "give me a chance" at a graveyard shift 'cause "you college girls are pretty smart," but the shift would end after the last bus left. It was a Chicano priest only blocks from my home that offered the answer. Father Rodríguez of Guadalupe Church (only one of many times that Guadalupe Tonantzín was to figure in my blessings) asked me to do a "strange job" (probably the best job I ever had). I was to collect folklore from my barrio, my beloved West Side Barrio, whose streets I would now hunt like a scavenger, zeroing in on unsuspecting viejitas y viejitos, who would prove to be my best and hardest professors. From there came many of my characters, much of my education; if it was anyone who "taught me to write," it was they.

I returned in the fall to my college to work on my Masters and to serve as the French teacher at Sherman High School. It was a gutsy and imaginative professor at Austin College, Dr. Virginia Love, who listened to my idealistic dreams about bilingual, multicultural education.

Then another fortunate turn. I was hired by Texas Lutheran College to be the Director of their Mexican American Studies Center. It's difficult for me to say now whether I invented the job or the job invented me, but it began my happy dive into all the denied areas of my childhood — delightful concepts that shook the earth and filled the soul, filled that vacuum of Latino Hunger — Chicano Literature, Bilingual Education, Mexican American History, Conversational Spanish of the Southwest — all the courses I taught were all the courses that taught me.

I worked my tail off, but absorbed the place and time like a sponge — it was the Movimiento Chicano, and I was hungering to push and move and dance and sweat and celebrate it forward. The next tool I discovered was the doctorate — a key that could open doors and help facilitate change. I wrote poetry in private (something I had done all my life, but with more *gusto* now) and became good friends with Reyes Cárdenas and Cecilio García-Camarillo. Later, my private poetry would go public, at the Floricantos and the Canto al Pueblos, and Alurista and Nephtalí, José Montoya, Angela de Hoyos, Inés Hernandez, and José Flores Peregrino would fill that celebration with a world of Chicano writers.

Other academic, writing, and administrative positions followed, but in each of the places — U.T., Fresno State, Southwest Labs, KLRN-TV, San Bernardino, Northern Arizona University, it was the people that shaped the bends and the turns of my career — it was the friendships that made the turning points. Other writers, like Yolanda Luera, Teresa Palomo Acosta, Ernesto Padilla, Harryette Mullen, Margarita Cota-Cárdenas, Rolando Hinojosa, Grady Hillman, Alex Haley, Carlos Fuentes, and Tomás Rivera, and special people who wrote poems with their lives like Emerenciano Rodríguez, Normando De Hallé, Ursula Knoki-Wilson, Francisco Alcocer, Tom and Lilly

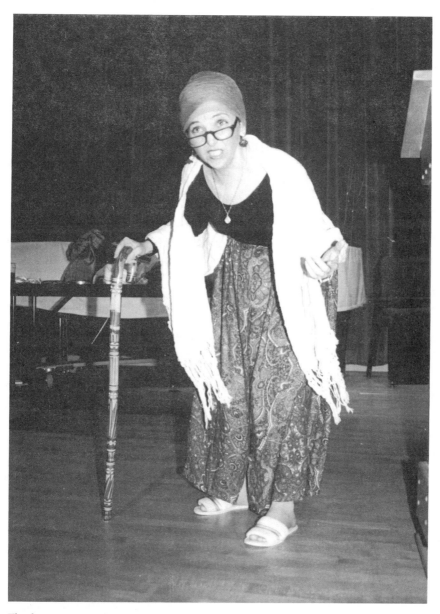

The character "Tía Sofía" as portrayed by Carmen Tafolla in the dramatic performance, <u>With Our Very Own Names</u>, *which has been presented throughout the United States, and in London, Madrid, Mexico City, Osnabrück, Germany, and Kristiansand, Norway.*

Rivera — these were the significant points of the job descriptions, the true honors behind the awards.

There were always three main sections to my professional work — the writing, the speaking engagement and consultant work, and the salaried position. But the last two always seemed to push the first out — when time was sacrificed, it was writing time. My conscience couldn't take this, because by then, I knew that, of the three, writing was the most important, and of the writing, the novel *La Gente* was already going into labor pains. I tried twice to "retire" from higher education (or *any* salaried position) — once when I left Fresno and an Associate Professor of Womens' Studies position ("But you could be chair in five years!" they pleaded. "I don't have five years to waste," I answered) and again when I left Northern Arizona University and a position as Special Assistant to the President. Time was a-wasting, and writing time does not "keep." I kept the speaking engagements and dramatic performances as a way to support my "writing habit," and also because the "sharing with people," the reading and speaking to audiences, made my writing more real, more connected, more purposeful.

People laughed about the "retirement" because no pension was connected to it, but I argued that if military are allowed to retire after twenty years, because of the high-risk nature of the work and the inherent stress of the front lines, then surely I should be allowed to retire after nineteen years of even harder front-line work in high-controversy, high-stress battlefields, speaking to nineteen-year-old frat rats about sexism, comfortable university administrators about racism, and rural Texas principals about bilingual education. I was tired of fighting the front lines in attitude change, I said. What I didn't tell them was that with writing, your mind is always on the front lines.

Last week, on the way home from an out-of-state speaking engagement, I decided that I would section off a part of my payment away from bill-paying and other "mandatories" and buy something I needed for the dramatic performance. I was filled with a sudden level of satisfaction, realizing that the job before this had also allowed me this spurt of determination, till I smiled in recognition of the voice — "Cómprate un fierro con cada día de pago." Only the definition of "día de pago" had had to be changed, to allow for the financial realities of larger "fierros," like computers, fileboxes, velas, and an occasional empty notebook.

Mi Familia

In 1979, in the oldest part of San Antonio, beside the river, in an old stone church that turned 100 that year, I married Ernesto Marroquín Bernal. We shared an illimitable love, values, a commitment to people, careers always intertwined with bilingualism-la cultura-and-education, and a strange mirroring of each other's lives. His father had been a Marine in WWII, mine a sailor. His mother had been a Protestant, his father a Catholic, and he was raised in a devout and idealistic Catholic childhood. My mother had been a Catholic, my father a Protestant, and I raised in a devout and idealistic Protestant childhood. He was the older of two boys, eleven years apart in age; I, the younger of two girls, ten years apart in age. He grew up speaking a formal Spanish and feeling quite comfortable with the Mexican upper and middle classes. I grew up with Tex-Mex as my native language and feeling most at

Tafolla's mother and grandmother – Mary Duarte Tafolla and Josefina Moreno De Duarte. "Our family has no set bounds and does not stop at the walls of our houses. It includes primos, *and* primos *three times removed,* abuelos, *aunts, uncles, and everyone's children."*

home with the Mexican lower classes. Both of us had grandmothers who spoke no English, who were not U.S. citizens, and who had an amazing *don* for healing; his grandmother had been a *maestra* in Mexico who had ended up working in a laundry in the U.S., mine had been a *criada* who had ended up being my first great teacher. The parallels were not visible to us at that time, only the love. Of all that my writing centers on people, it is hardest to write about him. He does not fit on the page, and no statement seems precise enough. He is, perhaps, like the description of his eyes, "de un color no patentado." The closest I have come to trying to express it was in the poems "y cuando pienso en tí," "¡Ajay!" and "No Tienes Limites."

Having children was something we had talked about since before even talking about marriage. It seemed right that love in such abundance should be shared. He was a single parent. Ann, 14, and Sean, 12, were at home. So the four of us dated and the four of us got married. We were excited about an expansion in family, but things happened differently from what we anticipated. There was no baby at the end of nine months, or even of eighteen. Finally, in early 1982, we were pregnant, and enjoying each minute of it. At six months of pregnancy, we discovered a problem — the child was in distress. The only alternative our doctor could offer was an immediate C-section of a very premature baby. The chances, we were told, were slim.

She was beautiful. And tiny. We named her the name we had selected months earlier for a girl — Cielos — for the freedom of the skies and the beauty of the heavens. We buried her in the old family cemetery, right next to the space reserved for my parents, one down from that of my grandparents, in a row with aunts and uncles and other members of the *familia*.

Losing Cielos was difficult. To lose a child is the deepest pain, the most awkward rub against the heart that expects our children to bury us, not us to bury them. My husband read Wordsworth's *We Are Seven* to me, the first I'd heard it, and sobbed. We mourned, and moved on, always taking her with us. She became my mentor and my teacher. She also became our *angelito*, bringing us several miracles. The greatest of these was a letter from Guadalajara, stating that a special child had been born, were we interested? We stumbled over each other in our haste to reach the phone and telegram "Definitivamente sí!" It was the spring of 1984.

She was not a replacement for Cielos, but, as we told her a few years later, she was picked by Cielos. As all the baby spirits went filing through heaven, preparing to be conceived, Cielos had seen her, had been struck by the beauty of her spirit, and had stated emphatically, "This is the one I want for my sister! This is the most beautiful spirit of all! Please, God, send her to my parents, by a special way." And Mother-Father God did. After a month's long distance calls to the American Embassy for a visa, we took an overnight flight, arrived in the waking hours of the dawn, and made a customs officer's day when he opened Ernesto's briefcase to find dozens of shiny metal caps on little bottles of white stuff glistening in the sunrise. Thinking he'd made the drug bust of the year, he smirked to me, "¿Y ésto?" "Fórmula," I responded, "¿Para bebé?" The exhausted officer slammed the briefcase shut and waved us past in disgust.

We were blessed with a child who opened those beautiful black diamond eyes (my mother's eyes) and recognized us, smiled and opened her arms to us. We named her Marilinda Tafolla Bernal, after my mother, María Duarte Tafolla and Ernesto's mother, Linda Marroquín Bernal. She had been born September 21, 1983, exactly a year and twelve days after Cielos, and, we were later to discover, she had been born exactly two-and-a-half months premature, like Cielos. But this whopping 3 pound, 3 ounce miracle survived. We were ecstatic with this spirited, strong, and terribly perceptive baby.

We did not know at the time that we were pregnant; a few months later we miscarried. It was not the right time, I guess. Two other times were also not the right time. After moving back to Texas in 1990 and trying to settle in, catch up, plant the necessary cilantro and hierba buena, and finish the *mentado* novel, we discovered to my ongoing shock that we were, at this late date, pregnant. A Passover-Easter spirit child, arriving once more, but at the right time, and midwifed by Mari's prayers for a younger brother or sister. On December 12, 1991, el día de la Virgen de Guadalupe, Israel Tafolla Bernal was born. It was a temptation to name him one of the old family names — Ernesto or Pedro, or Santiago, Mariano or Gabriel. But we picked instead an old traditional name of our *gente*, yet one we did not know of any family member who'd borne. "Is this your first child?" the nurses asked ("No sean ingenuas — tengo los cuarenta años, ¡muchachas sincesos!") "No . . ." I would answer, "He's either number 1 or 2 or 3 or 5, depending on how you count." I wasn't trying to be difficult — I was trying to be exact.

Yes, to some degree, with all this "familia" stuff, someone is sure to be justified in accusing me of being a hopeless romantic. Perhaps a traditional "wife-mother" type (my familia would laugh: they know of all the others who have criticized our commitment to a non-sexist marriage, but one that had to pick and choose its battles carefully because our society presented us with so many). Someone else is stereotyping me as one of those "breed-like-rats" Mexicans — "You let one move in and suddenly there's a dozen of them living there!" And sure enough, someone else is checking their notes that say that my

Some of the people who made up Tafolla's familia before she was born. "And when we speak of family, who can we really leave out?"

mother lives with us (she does, and we're all the luckier for it!), and that they remember in Flagstaff that we had an extra son, our primito-sobrinito-spiritual son, David Marroquín Hernández (or Hernández Marroquín, depending on which country you're in), who lived with us and added to the Christmas stockings that we hang every year, whether the family members are here or not. In most polite form, in as casual a tone as I would say "Assoyez-vouz," I will say: "Accusez-vous." Frankly, I don't care what they say. What I do care for are these people, these *familia*, these spirits, even these *gatos*, Dulce and Cariño, that share the house with the books and dreams, and human beings and pieces of nailed wood that serve as furniture. I recall a text that I wrote for a photo exhibit entitled "La Familia: The Strength of Our Culture" at The Institute of Texan Cultures in the early years after we were married:

> *La familia*, the family, is the source from which flows the strength of our culture. Our traditions, our *cuentos*, our values, our prayers, even the language that gives body to our feeling — all are kept, nurtured, developed and passed on, like weathered rich-wood heirlooms, in the tranquil timelessness of la familia. Our family has no set bounds and does not stop at the walls of our houses. It includes *primos*, and *primos* three times removed, *abuelos*, aunts, uncles and everyone's children.
>
> We draw others into our family — it becomes a warmth and a love. It becomes the supper table that feeds our soul at day's end; it becomes a homemade *caldo* of many ingredients, each one adding in their own way to the special flavor of its nurturing warmth.
>
> *La familia* . . . the strength of our culture is built on its quiet teachings, its unconditional love, the love it extends to newborn as to aged — love that is not parceled out according to what you do or what you have or how much you accomplish, but love for just being, *respeto por ser*. Its compassion and guidance show us the infinite gentleness of true strength.

The pictures of *la familia* are engraved forever in our hearts, but what our eyes touch must also be shared among ourselves and with each other. They must be as photographs that will never be forgotten.

But that only tells part of the story. Because we don't *have* photographs or even mental images of most of the people that form our familia — we don't even know who they were, or who they will be. And everything and everyone I see out there, and the even more numerous ones I don't see, are all the *real* members of my *familia*. And when we speak of family, who can we really leave out?

VI.
Criticism

With Our Very Own Names, or There Is Room Here For Two Tongues Inside This Kiss: The Voice of Carmen Tafolla

Ernesto Padilla
Santa Monica College

When first I called Carmen Tafolla and told her I wanted to write a paper on her poetry, I asked her suggestion as to the title. "With our very own names" came the response without hesitation. So be it. Most appropriate, yes. A manifesto every bit as provocative as Langston Hughes' bold proclamation of the 1920s, which announced that, henceforth, Black writers would honestly set forth their human condition and that both Anglos*and* Blacks would have to learn to look at poverty, despair, and violence along with love, creativity, and hope.[1] Tafolla's poetry and stories set forth the condition of women, of Chicanos, of the disenfranchised, and, like Afro-American literature in the Post-Harlem Renaissance period, her characters come alive with love, with movement, come alive with the very life that Jean-Paul Sartre so earnestly sought to achieve in his own writing: "To write was to engrave new being upon [the infinite tables of the word] or . . . to catch living things in the trap of phrases."

Let us see if Tafolla has caught living things in the "trap of phrases." The first part of the title of this paper comes from Tafolla's previously unpublished poem, "Porfiria":

> Porfiria doesn't exist
> but if she did
> she'd say "¡Qué se chingue Reagan!"
> "¡Rómpenles el borlote!"
> y "Tráigame una cerveza, Carlos."

Well, does Porfiria exist, or doesn't she? Here she is on the immortal page! She sits on committees saying, "Y que pendejos, porqué no?" and saying:

> "I handle too much shit
> to use a dust rag and
> furniture polish on it.
> Shovels work just fine."

---

[1] Here is the text of Hughes' manifesto: "We younger negro artists now intend to express our individual dark-skinned selves without fear or shame. If white people are pleased, we are glad. If they are not, it doesn't matter. We know we are beautiful and ugly, too. If colored people are pleased, we are glad. If they are not, their displeasure doesn't matter, either. We build our temples for tomorrow, strong as we know how, and we stand on top of the mountain, free within ourselves."

Original draft of second page of "Porfiria."

Our shock, astonishment, and admiration convince us that Porfiria *does* exist, but the poem closes with the reminder that she doesn't exist, concludes with a call to action:

Porfiria doesn't exist,
in the usual way,
    has no photograph,
    social security number,

or signature.
But Porfiria has just so damn much to say
that she will show up anyway, stubborn bitch,
that we will
    everyone of us
      take a picture
        invent a number
          sign a declaration
            for her
              even if it has to be
                with our very own
                  names.

Porfiria strikes at the gut: she embarrasses me and, yet, I am drawn to her. She is portrayed as illegitimate, with no Social Security number or signature. This poem is a call to arms for all Chicanas to "sign a declaration . . . with our very own names." Porfiria highlights, in the first instance, women who give up their surnames and take on an identity pleasing to men, who are defined by men. But, in a sense, she represents our repressed subconscious, a quelled instinct for honesty and right that dwells within us, all of us, both men and women. Let us be honest and accept that we admire assertiveness in all creatures big and small, male and female, and let us further accept that it pains us to tell our daughters that they can't aspire to realms beyond the feminine stereotype of selflessness, love, empathy, and nurturing.

If the brush strokes in "Porfiria" are elegant but not broad enough, they are swathed wider in "Federico y Elfiria,"* a story of a husband who decides that his wife is a "bad girl" and maybe even is having an affair because she begins to lustily and aggressively enjoy sex. This story is a hilarious caricature of men's neurosis and self-delusion that all women must be either madonnas or whores. By the end of the story, the reader is exasperated with Federico's naive immaturity and egocentric whining over whether Elfiria is a "good girl." We want to choke him, but Elfiria competently and lovingly takes command:

"¡Ya para con estas tonterías! Of course I'm a good girl! I'm more than that! Soy una madre — the mother of our child — y soy tu esposa — wife, you know. Like, married?"

Here we have humor and irony, situational irony. The only one that doesn't realize his smallness of mind is Federico:

Federico had never thought of it that way. He had always heard of — pos, tú sabes — d'esas, bad girls, y también of course de good girls — but of someone being a good girl plus more? Maybe that explained it.
. . .] He hadn't figured it out completely, pero Elfiria interrupted him and said, "¡Ya olvídate de esas cosas! Let's go to bed!" And they did, and pos, tú sabes, a man can only do so much all by himself.

---

*A movie is currently being made of this hilarious story (scheduled for release in 1996).

Elfiria? Porfiria? We have here the birth of a new character, neither madonna nor whore.[2] Porfiria kills Virginia Woolf's "angel of the house," that same "angel of the house"[3] that drives Edna Pontillier in Kate Chopin's *The Awakening* to suicide, that same "angel of the house" that ensures serious psychosomatic illness and suppression of genius in Alice James. Porfiria is a "sassy" lady who appears throughout Tafolla's poetry — not with the same name, but always with that same "lusty," down-home, upbeat attitude. See, for example, the erotic, sensuous poem, "October 21st, 9 p.m. (autumn, she don't waste no time!)" Here the autumn night sky is personified:

> [. . .] and her breezes pant strong
>> she works hard
>>> plays hard
>>>> breathes deep

>>>> blows the useless stuff away —
>>>>> like leaves
>>>>>> from seasons
>>>>>>> past

>>>> looks to the root
>>>> goes for the gut

>>>> lays her earthy soul

>>>> right up against her lover-man earth

>>>>> with nothin'

>>>>>> in

>>>>>> between'm.

Here is the feminine consciousness unafraid, in full control of metaphor and personification, swallowing life.

There are horrors that elegant poetry and incisive humor will not obviate. Men can also hate women with such violence that they will rape, brutalize, dismember, and murder. This is not to diminish the aesthetics, the sensibility, the poetic power evident in "Porfiria," "Autumn she don't waste no time," and "Federico and Elfiria." Instead, lest the reader think that Tafolla's portraits lack peripheral vision, that they ignore the most brutal forms of oppression

---

[2] Of course this "new" character is not new at all. The women's liberation movement goes back several centuries to Sor Juana Inéz de la Cruz in Latin America and over a century in the United States. In literature, we have outstanding examples in Sor Juana Inéz de la Cruz, Kate Chopin (*The Awakening*) and Virginia Woolf (*A Room of One's Own, To the Light House*), Chaucer ("The Wife of Bath") and Sophocles (*Antigone*). In Chicana literature, we should notice landmark poetry of the 1960's and 1970s by Angela de Hoyos, Margarita Cota-Cárdenas, Lorna Dee Cervantes, and Bernice Zamora. See Tey Diana Rebolledo's important article "The Maturing of Chicana Poetry: The Quiet Revolution of the 1980s" for historical discussion of Chicana literature and its influences. Part of a Cota-Cárdenas poem is cited at the end of this paper.

[3] Woolf eloquently gives a local habitation and a name to the "Angel in the House": "The shadow of her wings fell on my page; I heard the rustling of her skirts in the room." See Woolf's article "Professions for Women" in *The Death of the Moth and Other Essays*.

imposed on women, here is a poem that convinces one of the futility of the patriarchal formula for "protecting" women:

Sweet Remember[4]

Sweet Remember
when you ask your little girls to be
so sweet,
sit neat,
cry easy,
and be oh so pretty on a shelf

When our young women who are decent
are to always be
in company
of strong young men

[. . .]

Sweet Remember
Elsa B.
whose naked 3-year daughter
was immersed
in ice-cold water,
as the Sergeant pulled her tits and whispered in her ear,
"Whore, come sleep with me
and do it sweetly
or we will not let
the child's head up
until she kicks no more."
And when she did,
they threatened a
Portrait in Two:
Whore and Child Whore —
side by side in bed —
with plenty volunteers
to tear them both
right through the core

[. . .]

And Sweet Remember
young Anita S.
who was raised to think her womanhood
was in her breasts

---

[4] Although the passages quoted here are a bit long, they only represent about a fourth of this previously unpublished poem.

and inside panties and to be covered
in a dress
and then,
because the village teacher was
a critic
of the government,
and a family friend,
she was "detained,"
and called a Marxist,
had her breasts
slashed at with knives
and bit by soldiers eager
for their flesh
and had then "Communist"
burnt with electric pen
and shocks
into her upper thigh,
and her vagina
run by mice,

[. . .]

But I will teach her
quite instead
that she is her own brave life
till dead
and that there are no guarantees in life
nor rights
but those that we invent [. . . .]

These explicit passages leave little room for debate. Here is the extreme case, a horrific chronicle of documented atrocities (Tafolla found these atrocities reported in an Amnesty International report).

If Porfiria and Elfiria do not convince one that "womanhood was in her soul," the narrator of "Sweet Remember" does convince. The gruesome and sobering atrocities depicted here speak for themselves. The major achievement of the poem lies in the courage to confront and depict that which humanity would deny, that which causes us to grimace, wince, and avert our gaze (we would prefer, instead, to, as Chaucer writes in "The Nun's Priest's Tale," "dreme alday of owles or of apes / And of many a maze therwithal"). But we are forced to look: here is a sustained look. The narrator speaks to the reader, persuasively convinces that one should teach women to learn to protect themselves, that there are sick men who find innocence inviting, that women must assertively and bravely "invent" their own salvation. Some men have learned to expect treachery and violence: they distrust appearances, and chivalry is but a parlor game, but women are too often taught to never expect treachery and violence. "Sweet Remember" is a brutal teacher that contextualizes the problematic of sexism and feminism. It sets forth the seldom spoken parameters.

Beyond its honesty, this poem has simplicity (short lines often consisting of just one or two words) and persuasive rhythm (note that long lines speed up the tempo of the poem, "that she is her own brave life," and short lines appropriately slow down the tempo, "'till dead").

The most important aesthetic aspect of the poem is its unflinching tone of honesty: "here are the brutal facts. These things happen," it announces. Perhaps it is in the aspect of "tone," the rhetorical device of "tone," with which Tafolla "kills the angel in the house." "Sweet Remember" is a poem that goes beyond Woolf's accomplishment, a poem that demonstrates how far late twentieth century women have gone beyond Woolf's daring, beyond Woolf's fear of the total baring of the feminine soul:

> These then were two very genuine experiences of my own. These were two of the adventures of my professional life. The first — killing the Angel in the House — I think I solved. She died. But the second, telling the truth about my own experiences as a body, I do not think I solved. ("Professions for Women")

There can be little doubt that this numbing poem tells the truth about women's bodies, not that Tafolla is the first (women have now been doing this both in literature and in pop culture since the late '60's), but that Tafolla's voice adds resonance to this rising tide — this necessary first step — of the "telling the truth" (raising consciousness) crescendo. Almost a contradiction in terms, isn't it, such spare, spare resonance? But it is the tone and not prosodic convolutions that haunts the reader's mind with such rich resonance. Yes, it is this tone of both respect for, and assertiveness toward men that dumbfounds: the narrator is saying to patriarchal society, "You have had the education of women in hand, now 'I will teach her quite instead.'"

In the latter half of the twentieth century, we have become accustomed to contemplating womanhood in quite a different way. Let us compare the attitude in "Sweet Remember" with that, for example, of a man who knows that he has been damned to eternal perdition, a man whose pendulum swings between despair, anguish, self-hatred, and a lusty appreciation of the greatest joys of earthly life. Here is the depraved sixteenth century conjurer Dr. John Faustus about to fulfill the "greatest" fantasy of a group of fellow scholars:

> Master Doctor Faustus, since our conference about fair ladies, which was the beautifullest in all the world, we have determined with ourselves that Helen of Greece was the admirablest lady that ever lived. Therefore, Master Doctor, if you will do us that favor as to let us see that peerless dame of Greece whom all the world admires for majesty, we should think ourselves much beholding unto you. (5.1.11–17)

Here a group of scholars, philosophers, and scientists from a great Renaissance German university who have spent many serious hours contemplating the greatest things in heaven and on earth find their curiosity and pleasure to be not the depraved condition of the conjurer's soul, but the legendary beauty of one woman. We would hope that this perpetual return to the contemplation of women, especially in this instance (Christopher Marlowe's great Elizabethan play), is more spiritual than carnal, but it is not. Marlowe establishes the legendary beauty of Helen as the yardstick by which we are to measure the worth of all women. This lust for the carnal aspects of women diminishes all women and men: all women after Helen suddenly become second choice and all men become those who will put up with second choice.

And yet, the contemplation of beauty is of the highest order. There is beauty in the human spirit, in the human imagination. Such is the case in Tafolla's "Sweet Remember." All of us who are prone to contemplate "beauty" will find that the narrator of "Sweet Remember" conceives of a woman of a higher order than Helen, a woman of intelligence, courage, a woman of astounding inner beauty. In "Sweet Remember," as in "Porfiria," we find a consciousness that will not be tricked by appearances, a consciousness that seeks a new order. In Tafolla's poetry we find the "fairest" ladies of the highest nobility, strong, yet loving women who will redefine the roles of both sexes with love, honesty, humility, and courage. These women are role-models. Here is the ideal that Faustus would have appreciated. He would have appreciated this new protaganist because she fulfills John Keats' requirement for beauty: "beauty overcomes every other consideration, or rather obliterates all consideration." In "To Miss Cole," Tafolla goes even further, shaking the very guage of beauty, as women stand before a mirror and finally conclude, "that mirror – it funny shape too."

Tafolla's poetic skills are impressive, and when she turns her pen to humor and wit, it becomes obvious that she may soon enter the company of America's great humorists. We have an inkling of this humor in an early poem, "Tía Sofía":

"Remember that time at the lake, con Sofía?
— Sophie! Come out of the water! It's raining!
— No, me mojo! (I'll get wet!)"

"Tía Sofía" is a mixture of both irreverence and naiveté.

"Quality Literature," also replete with humor and irony, is the story of a young student who wants to study meaningful literature that reflects his life experience: literature by Chicanos. But the arrogant, intellectual professor, Dumont, ("in his crisp pseudo-British accent") wants the student to study Samuel Beckett's *Waiting for Godot* because there "simply hasn't been any quality Chicano literature." The student persists, mentioning several works by Chicano writers. Dumont comments that he has not heard of any of those Chicano writers and that they have not "even been critiqued in the PMLA! And until it's critiqued in the PMLA, I can't say it's quality literature!" At this point, Dumont begins to recall who this stubborn, presumptuous student is:

... said the professor, examining with slight curiosity the face
of the student whom he now faintly recalled as having made
very poor marks on the last exam. "Of course," he thought.

Naturally, Dumont browbeats the student with his intellectuality and authority, and walks off "into a semi-colon . . . as the face of the student" becomes an "epic poem." Here we have irony at its best. The student's indomitable spirit, the student's persistent valuation of Chicano culture is poetic, and the student's inevitable disillusionment speaks for many. "Quality Literature" is an epic poem worth writing, and Carmen Tafolla has written it.

Although both "Tía Sofía" and "Quality Literature" are early works, they are admirable and well done. However, the short, short story, "You Don't Know Marta," is a masterpiece. Here is another of Tafolla's irreverent and lusty stories, spare and to the point. The narrator begins by announcing that she is prejudiced: "Now I might as well be honest an' tell you right now that I'm prejudiced. I think San Antonio is the absolute center of the universe." The reader's anxiety over a potential story of race prejudice is immediately defused. This is a friendly story where we can let our "hair down, an' jus' talk" (the vernacular — "Más viva que una víbora" — is delightful throughout).

And yet, this story is about prejudice after all: sexism. The Chicano community leaders have invited the narrator's husband, Ernie, to an all-male *tardeada* (an outdoor dinner party). However, Ernie doesn't realize that it is an exclusive party and takes the narrator to the *tardeada*. The leadership has previously agreed not to speak to any woman in attendance because of a rumor that a Chicana women's organization is planning to "crash" the party. The narrator and husband arrive and only one of the ninety-four "squinty eyed thorns" talks to them: this is Arnulfo, who wears glasses so thick that they "give him a different sight from everyone else." The narrator and her husband go home, and sometime later, the husband receives an invitation for next year's *tardeada* ("all-male *tardeada*. No women. No Anglos allowed."), and he "jus' put[s] it at the bottom of our stack of bills paid."

The punch line of the story is foreshadowed by the title in combination with a hyperbole where Ernie asserts that, if Marta were to step outside the city limits, the average IQ of the city of Austin would "drop by 15 points." The narrator then asserts that "you might think that was a slight exaggeration, but then you don't know Marta." But it is obvious that if this story is well conceived, we must also close with Marta. After putting the "fancy engraved invitation" to the Chicano leader's *tardeada* (where "great ideas" are born) at the bottom of the bills paid stack, the narrator ends with "We'd already been to one *tardeada* an' if you think all the leaders were there, then you jus' don't know Marta."

"You Don't Know Marta" is a story of invitation, a love story, a love for humanity. The narrator and her husband form a community with Marta and Arnulfo (the one "cactus flower" among the cactus thorns) and invite the reader, regardless of sex or ethnicity, to join in mutual respect and love. Here,

Tafolla has fulfilled Sandra Gilbert and Susan Gubar's prediction. In an analysis of Jane Austen's *Persuasion*, Gilbert and Gubar conclude that "women themselves have the power to create themselves as characters, even perhaps the power to reach toward the woman trapped on the other side of the mirror/text and help her to climb out" (16).

Two nineteenth century novels that portray an independent woman are Flaubert's *Madame Bovary* and Kate Chopin's *The Awakening*. Both attempt a profound and sympathetic psychological study of the awakening consciousness of a woman trapped in patriarchal reality, both characters, like Antigone, precipitate their destruction, but Flaubert's protagonist conforms to (and thereby confirms) social law (literary paternity: women are either madonnas or whores), whereas Chopin's character rewrites social law, suggests the awakening strength of the new woman. Tafolla's characters have the power and assertiveness of Chopin's Edna and Sophocles' Antigone, but they succeed, they are role models for independent thinking, joy, and gusto, and because her portrayals are presented, essentially, via humor, Tafolla escapes the social wrath that seeks to silence the "intemperate." She overcomes the double bind of feminist story tellers as articulated clearly by Gilbert and Gubar:

> a life of feminine submission, of "contemplative purity," is a life of silence, a life that has no pen and no story, while a life of female rebellion, of "significant action," is a life that must be silenced, a life whose monstrous pen tells a terrible story. (36)

Although my students wince at some feminist portraits and argue vociferously, they unanimously enjoy Tafolla's stories and poems.

Tafolla's invitation to honesty, to simplicity, to humility is once more powerfully wrought in the compelling poem, "Poquito allá." Here, the protagonist is centered, and has a positive, salutary self-image. He has lost some fingers of his right hand, but is happy that he can still shake hands and embrace others in friendship. This humble protagonist is physically disfigured, but his spirit is whole while the Anglo who disfigured this Mexican-American peasant is physically whole but disfigured in spirit, an ironic and illuminating reversal of John Donne's elegant articulation of the Calvinist concept that depravity was somehow outwardly discernable: "To wicked spirits are horrid shapes assign'd / This beauteous forme assures a piteous minde," (from the ninth sonnet, "What if this present were the world's last night?"). "Poquito allá" presents us with a horrid shape that contains a sublime "minde."

Returning to Tafolla's invitation, her invitation to honest community is the greatest of her themes. Her work continually invites us to touch our "fingers tip to tip / and say that we were blood and human voice and friend" (from the beautifully lyric sonnet, "How Shall I Tell You?"). Tafolla tells us with eloquence in "hay un lugar" that "There is a place / where corn is ground by daily arms / and old metate smoothed by flow of family," a place where

[. . .] adobe walls

retain the day's high sun
and spread its warmth so kindly
through the night,

a place where "even zopilotes have a softness to their name." Tafolla's
poetry invites softly with the redundancy of the invitation:

hay un lugar
donde hay un lugar para tí

Notice the humility and the warmth of the invitation: the title is all lower
case (typically in Spanish the title of poems are in the lower case with the
exception of the first word of the title). Only the English translation, "There
is a place" bears the capital letter. The Spanish is encantatory, is warm with
the familiar "tí." How could we refuse this place "where corn is ground by daily
arms" and the "old metate smoothed by flow of family"? What aesthetic
sensibility where "daily arms" grind the corn where the "old metate" allitera-
tively soothes by "flow of family"! We are in the presence of an artist of high
sensibility which we can trust because she sees more than we do and teaches
with competence and love, a love that works like adobe walls (that retain
warmth) to spread her understanding through the dark, cold human night.
This love is a full-bodied love, a love that acknowledges lusty range, as is
evident in this recent poem:

Chaucer must have felt like this,
    the old Pachuco playing his TexMex onto the page
and even then the critics said,
    "Write
    in one language"
But he looked at all that cleanness, so controlled,
    forms halved, and just could not deny
his own familia, primos from both sides,
                weeds that liked to crawl
                over sidewalks, pa' juntarse,
                visit, stretch out comfy,
                natural and lusty,
                hybrid wealth,
    [. . .]
But
You, like they,
want Shaker hallways
and I grow Mexican gardens and backyards.
There are 2 many colors in the marketplace
to play modest, when Mexico and
Gloria Rodríguez say,
"¡Estos gringos con su Match-Match,
y a mí me gusta Mix-Mix!"

There are 2 many cariños to be
                created
to stay within the lines,
2 many times
when I want to tell you:
                There is room
                        here
                    for two
                    tongues
                inside this
                    kiss.

In this poem, Tafolla praises the rebellious creative genius of Geoffrey
Chaucer, of whom it has been said that he stood "apart from the mainstream
of English literature," and that "English poetry had little to teach the first great
English poet" (Abrams 90-91). In his *Canterbury Tales*, Chaucer abandons the
Old English poetic line with its characteristic caesura (breaking of the line
into two halves) and inter-stitching by means of alliteration, abandons this
caesuric line in favor of the iambic pentameter line; indeed, Chaucer may well
have been the first English poet to use the iambic pentametric line. Tafolla
praises "hybrid wealth," both in the poetic line (specifically the linguistic code
switching from English to Spanish, as well as the prosodic experimentation
that approximates the Chicano vernacular) and in the culture (the positive
valorization of the intermingling of the North American, Mexican, and
Native American cultures: "a mí me gusta Mix-Mix" — I like to Mix-Mix).

It is not hard to see why Tafolla was awarded first prize at the 1987
University of California, Irvine National Chicano Literature Contest. Carmen
Tafolla and so many other talented Chicana writers are creating vibrant
literature with their "very own names."

Tafolla's theme of self assertiveness, "with our very own names," echoes
Margarita Cota-Cárdenas' evocative call of the 1970's (in *Noches despertando
in Conciencias*):

busca tu nombre
    dentro de tí misma
Chicana
    crea tu propia palabra
    tu esencia TU
[. . .]
sea homenaje a tu raza, crea tu propio cosmos
CHICANA HERMANA MUJER
    ahora actua por
        TI

A translation is offered by Tey Diana Rebolledo ("The Maturing of
Chicana Poetry: The Quiet Revolution of the 1980s," 158):

Look for your name
     inside your own self
Chicana
     create your own word
     your essence YOU

[. . .]

be a credit to your race, create your own cosmos
CHICANA SISTER WOMAN
     now act for
        YOURSELF

Like the great African-American woman writers (Toni Morrison, Alice
Walker, and Zora Neale Hurston) Carmen Tafolla and other Chicana writers
are showing promise of more density, more substance, more vivacity than their
male counterparts. Yes, Carmen Tafolla, it is necessary that you and so many
others assure that the world hears Porfiria's voice, and you will only accom-
plish this if you write with your very own names. It is also salutary to hear your
eloquent voice say que "hay un lugar para tí," to know that you invite us all to
touch fingers "tip to tip," to see you insist that

There is room
        here
      for two
      tongues
    inside this
       kiss.

WORKS CITED

Abrams, M. H., et. al., ed. *The Norton Anthology of English Literature: Volume
    1* (5th ed.). London: W. W. Norton & Company, 1986.
Cota-Cárdenas, Margarita. *Noches despertando in Conciencias*. Tucson: Scor-
    pion Press, 1975, n.p.
Gilbert, Sandra and Susan Gubar. *The Mad Woman in the Attic.*
Marlowe, Christopher. *The Tragical History of the Life and Death of Doctor
    Faustus*. London: W. W. Norton & Company, 1986, 814-65.
Rebolledo, Tey Diana. "The Maturing of Chicana Poetry: The Quiet Revolu-
    tion of the 1980s" in *For Alma Mater: Theory and Practice in Feminist
    Scholarship*, ed. Paula A. Treichler, et. al.
Woolf, Virginia. "Professions for Women," in *The Death of the Moth and Other
    Essays*. Harcourt Brace Jovanovich, Inc. (1942)

Code-Switching as Metaphor in Chicano Poetry

Cordelia Candelaria
University of Colorado at Boulder

The poetic imagination is as persistent as a cactus flower. Despite the awesome strength of the forces that challenge it, that imagination persists in expressing its specific truths and impressions clearly visible in Chicano poetry, a body of the literature of the Americas that has lived, and even flourished, quietly for over a century. Not only has Chicano poetry suffered the blistering hostility of a U.S. literary tradition that would deny the legitimacy of non-British origin, non-English language forms, it also has had to endure the indifference of a publishing industry content to promote literature patterned only in recognizable Yankee forms, however esoteric and avant-garde they might be. But though Mexican-American poets and their audiences may be seen as victims of a harsh literary environment, Chicano poetry itself is neither victim nor loser. It is, rather, a testament to *chicanismo* — to its vast and multifold riches, as well as to its dynamic and irrepressible creativity.

The attributes resonate with special strength and timbre in the language of Chicano poetry, particularly in its multilingualism, that polyphonic code of sound and sense that ramifies out of at least six different language systems. For background reference, they are:

1. Standard edited American English;
2. English slang (regional dialects and vernaculars including varieties of Black English);
3. Standard Spanish;
4. Dialectal Spanish (regional vernaculars including caló);
5. English/Spanish or Spanish/English blends of bilingualism; and
6. An amalgam of pre-American indigenous langauges, mostly noun forms from Nahuatl and Mayan.

Moreover, Chicano poetry manifests a variety of combinations of these six systems so that a given poem, like Chicano bilingual speech, might disclose yet another, different combination form, and so on. *The point is that the phonological, morphological, syntactic, and semantic possibilities of Chicano poetry are astonishingly flexible and extensive.*

To demonstrate one aspect of these remarkable possibilities, this paper examines one linguistic area of Chicano poetry, its code-switching. My thesis is that code-switching in Chicano poetry is emblematic of theme. That is, specific transition itself — the discrete speech act of changing from one language to another and back again — conveys meaning quite apart from the lexical meanings denoted or the symbolic meanings connoted by the surface language forms. The thesis is best argued through application, for which I have chosen a well-known poem by Alurista and a less familiar but more recent piece by Carmen Tafolla. These texts were selected to illustrate some of the different kinds of code-switching found in Chicano poetry. In Alurista's piece, the code-switching presents two languages in separate syntactic units, each operating independently of the other, whereas Tafolla's intermixes two languages interdependently within a syntactic unit. Scholars have described these two types as, respectively, *bilingual* and *interlingual* (Bruce-Novoa, 1982, 226).

"address"

address
occupation
age
marital status
— perdone. . .
yo me llamo pedro
telephone
height
hobbies
previous employers
— perdone. . .
yo me llamo pedro
pedro ortega
zip code
i.d. number
classification
— perdone mi padre era
el señor ortega
(a veces don josé)
race

Alurista (*Floricanto en Aztlán*, 1971)

Written in plain, elemental language, "address" lacks the figurative multiplicity typical of Alurista's best known style, with its pervasive use of pre-American motifs, images of *mestizaje*, and references to the Chicano Movement. Here, the simplicity of the diction and its many repetitions achieve a formulaic minimalism that underscores the poem's thematic focus on the failure of communication in a bureaucratic society. To convey his theme, Alurista relies on code-switching to contrast the two languages and, by extension, the cultures they represent. For instance, the English language portion consists almost entirely of nouns — no verbs, articles, or any trace of grammatical syntax — whereas the Spanish, though given fewer lines, evinces a grammatical completeness that underscores its semantics and thus heightens the difference between idioms, a difference extending far beyond language.

Like other Phase II Chicano poems (Candelaria, 1986, 71), "address" deals with the insensitivity of a modern bureaucracy that has become as impersonal as the machine-produced forms it uses to spindle and mutilate the people it is supposed to serve. On one level the poem duplicates the attempted communication between a Mexican (or Chicano) and a bureaucrat so inured to the surrounding Orwellian routine that s/he resembles a machine. Through metonymy, however, the poem demonstrates on another level the sterile impersonality of Yankee culture in its dominance over ethnic minorities. Pedro Ortega, a metonym for all colonized raza, wishes to identify himself by reference to his name, his father, and his father's respectability. But his inquisitor perceives him solely in terms of external variables associated with an easily categorized, superficial identification. As a result, the dialogue is at best parallel, not interactive, and they fail to communicate.

Yet having asserted the foregoing in discussing the poem's theme, one must ask: *Why is this so? Where in the text does one prove it?* Certainly nothing in the English words themselves denotes cultural polarity of values. Perhaps Pedro Ortega is meant to be seen as deranged and absurdly talking to himself while completing a form of some sort. To take such an alternative reading seriously, however, would be to seriously undermine the poem's considerable merit. Instead, we must conclude that the overall meaning depends directly on the English to Spanish code-switching that occurs four times in the available linguistic choices and permits him to allude to both the dominant Anglo and the minority Chicano cultures efficiently. Thus, despite its brevity and because of the code-switching, "address" manages to reflect a considerable range of U.S. society. Especially effective is the final shift, which carefully isolates "race" in the last line to draw dramatic attention to the fundamental significance of race and racism in U.S. American society. Its isolation confirms what the rest of the poem implies — that despite the strengths and richnesses of his culture, Señor Ortega is precluded from socioeconomic opportunities primarily because of his race, which also precludes meaningful interaction with either the bureaucracy or the dominant culture that produced it.

"woman-hole":

Some say there is a
vacuum — a black hole —
   in the center of womanhood
    that swallows countless
     secrets and has strange
      powers

Yo no sé desas cosas
solo sé que the
    black echo is music
        is sister of sunlight
            and from it
                crece
                vida.

Carmen Tafolla
(*Revista Chicano-Riqueña*, 1983)

The first stanza of Tafolla's poem sets up the straw man of patriarchal tradition regarding the reputed eternal mystery of women and the mystique of femininity. Employing paradox to draw attention to the conflicting perceptions of women characteristic of that tradition, Tafolla exposes the bizarre contradictions within those perceptions. For example, there is paradox in her title, which is at once a crude reference to a part of female physiology and also an emblem of the romanticization of "Woman" throughout the ages. There is paradox, too, in the yoking of "vacuum" (i.e., "a black hole" signifying nothingness) with the capacity (i.e., somethingness) to consume "countless secrets" arising out of the "strange powers." The one would seem to cancel the other. Extending the paradox to the second stanza, the poet introduces an outwardly humble "yo" who asserts ignorance of the conceptualizations just described, but who then immediately proceeds to exhibit enough sophistication to indulge in synesthetic and oxymoronic comparisons. By reducing the first stanza's concepts to mere "cosas," the speaker cleverly reverses history's reductive objectification of women, whether on pedestal or pillory, throughout the centuries. Tafolla then offers her own "woman-hole" metaphors in the synthesthetic of sound ("echo") and sight ("sunlight") and the oxymoron of darkness ("black") being "sister" to daughter ("sunlight"). She switches again to Spanish in the concluding lines, which affirm the literal fact that "from it / crece / vida." Also contributing to the metaphor is the poem's print pattern suggestive of womb and vagina, as well as the hourglass figure of male fantasy against which the female form has traditionally been measured. Through these techniques, the poet makes concrete the idea that self-definition by women is a requisite prelude to self-discovery of our literal worth.

Crucial to this reading of "Woman-Hole" is a thematic interpretation of its code-switching, for it alone accounts for the distinct separation of the speaker from those who "say there is a vacuum . . . in the center of womanhood." The interlingualism in stanza two emphasizes the speaker's separate identity as an individual woman whose self-perception derives from such primal elements as music and sunlight. (Parenthetically, these elements are themselves symbols of two fundamental kinds of life, the creative and the procreative.) The shift to an interlingual idiom distances the speaker and, logically, all her "sister[s]" from the standard canons accountable for the sexist language and thought that are the implicit subjects of stanza one. Without the

intermixing of languages, the poem might still aptly capture the contradictions within the patriarchal objectification of estrangement from the civilization that produced her.

Accordingly, Tafolla's code-switching brings to the foreground a contrast
between what Mircea Eliade describes as the diurnal and the nocturnal modes
of mind — that is, the rationality of conscious thought vs. the intuition of
subconscious insight (Eliade, 1959). According to Eliade, the epistemological
goal is a dynamic balance between modes to account inclusively for the wide
variety of experience and discourse in any age. Both Tafolla and Alurista
achieve, I believe, that kind of dynamic inclusivity. Tafolla suggests the strict
rationality of the diurnal mode in her first stanza's scientific "vacuum" and
"black hole," but she reverses it to pseudo-science in the last three lines of that
stanza. The reversal establishes a context for the next stanza's interlingual
switch to the nocturnal mode, with its metaphorical comparison that derives
from the intuitive artistry of the subconscious. A similar polarity appears in
Alurista's "address." The English language lines capture the cold sterility of a
totally dehumanized diurnal rationality incapable of engaging the subjective,
intuitive faculties of emotion and familiar identity. Oppositely, the Spanish
lines suggest the fuller, more holistic nocturnal mode reaching back to a more
primal humanistic tradition. The code-switching in both poems makes the
contrast of perspective particularly salient.

The skin of language is the only universally shared system that can cover
every facet of multitudinous experience. Language is the only skin large
enough to be shared, but when we try to objectify it for empirical analysis, the
result is much like Fausto Tejada's experience in *The Road to Tamazunchale*
when he peels off his skin and finds that its mass is so small he can place it in
the palm of his hand. The narrow structuralist study of language sometimes
yields about as much as Fausto's skin: a palm-full of alphabet representing a
taxonomy of phonemes that constitute the skin of communication. But
language is vastly, complexly more than the skin itself. It is simultaneously the
externalization of experience, both private and shared, past and present,
actual and imagined, while it is also what defines and records that experience.
Hence, to comprehend the multilayered nature of experience captured in
Chicano poetry requires that any analysis of the poetry be attentive to its
linguistic categories.

In this paper I have sought to apply such attention to one linguistic aspect
of two poems to demonstrate the thematic centrality of code-switching in
itself and quite apart from other linguistic elements and categories. These
titles join countless others in illustrating that code-switching in Chicano
poetry, whether bilingual or interlingual, (a) enriches the linguistic reper-
toire, (b) alludes to culture, (c) reflects the social matrix, (d) asserts an
ethnocultural autonomy, and (e) manifests the dichotomy of values implicit
in the diurnal vs. the nocturnal modes of mind. Consequently, like other
metaphors, the act of code-switching must be comprehended not only as a
linguistic vehicle for literary expression, but as a multiplicitous symbolic

element of the text.

WORKS CITED

Alurista, *Floricanto en Aztlán*. Los Angeles: UCLA Chicano Studies Research Program, 1971.

_____, *Return: Alurista Poems Collected and New*, Gary Keller, ed. Ypsilanti, Michigan: Bilingual Press/Editorial Bilingüe, 1982.

Bruce-Novoa, Juan. *Chicano Poetry: A Response to Chaos*. Austin: University of Texas Press, 1982.

Candelaria, Cordelia. *Chicano Poetry, A Critical Introduction*. Westport, Connecticut: Greenwood Press, 1986.

_____, *Ojo de la Cueva/Cave Springs*. Colorado Springs, Colorado: Maize Press, 1984.

Eliade, Mircea. *The Sacred and Profane*. N.Y.: Harper Torchbooks, 1959.

Gumperz, John J. and Dell Hymes, eds. *Directions in Sociolinguistics*. New York: Holt, Rinehart and Winston, 1972.

Gunn, Giles. *The Interpretation of Otherness: Literature, Religion and the American Imagination*. New York: Oxford University Press, 1979.

Martínez, Julio A. and Francisco A. Lomelf, eds. *Chicano Literature: A Reference Guide*. Westport, Connecticut: Greenwood Press, 1985.

Tafolla, Carmen, et al. *Get Your Tortillas Together*. San Antonio, Texas: S/A Publications, 1976.

Vigil, Evangelina, ed. "Woman of Her Word: Hispanic Women Write." *Revista Chicano-Riqueña*. 11:3-4 (1983).

Uncouth, Unkist

Alicia Chavez Francis
Santa Monica College

In the poem, "Right In One Language," as well as in her other works, Carmen Tafolla has shed light on the importance of revering cultural heritage and diversity in the restoration and maintenance of individual and collective identities.

Tafolla weaves language into a richly figured tapestry with a hybrid quality by making use of the language of the people. Her writing has all the brilliance of a sarape and the strength and resilience of a carefully crafted patchwork quilt, a fine blending of two cultures. Tafolla uses language to depict the texture of human nature in a true manner. Oscar Wilde has suggested that "Thought and language are to the artist instruments of an art" (xiii-xiv), and it is clear that Tafolla, in "Right In One Language," has the instruments of her art well in hand.

"Right In One Language" is a two-tempo poem. Tafolla moves the reader through an angry denouncement of conformity in a *tempo commodo*; that is, a moderate tempo. Then, she escalates the reader's imagination to the beat of a *tempo dibello* in a jubilant celebration of freedom.

Conformity is but a means of controlling and labeling that which is foreign or unknown. Moderation in the written word is not an effective approach to moving the imagination. This poem shows how conformity and moderation can create a wall, rendering the writer's mind blank.

> say, "It's not French, is it?"
> But it isn't.
> Nor is my mind
> when I try tight, clean line
> manicured to be like Leave
> it to Beaver's house
>   straight sidewalk
>   so square hedges
>   and if there's one on
> this   side there's also one on   that
> Equally paced
>   placed
>   spaced

controlled

The allusion to Beaver's house (from the *Leave It To Beaver* television show), along with the spatial placement and alliterative use of words, gives the reader an accurate visualization of how the mind, her mind, is stifled by too much control.

Tafolla invites the reader to lose control. To the pace of a *tempo dibello*, the reader realizes the intense feeling of the dynamic energy in freedom. The reader celebrates. Tafolla celebrates. She relishes the presentation of her whole being — two worlds, two cultures. The baseball bat explodes the piñata, sprinkling her pages with a wealth of treasures from two worlds. "[I]n this one,' he says, 'it all explodes.' I see bilingüe-beautiful explosions — two worlds collide."

Tafolla likens herself to Chaucer. He, like her, did not meet the critics' standards. He, like her, did not write for just one person, but for everyone,

    and told them it was just because
    he was undisciplined
            unpolished
                and did not know
                    how to make love
                    with just
                    one
                    person
                    in the room
                    or
                    on the page

    And he, like me,
    did what he wanted anyway

Tafolla and Chaucer, for the love of their art and humanity, were both willing to forgo the critics' blessing. Considered by others a libertine, Chaucer accepted his fate: "Uncouth, unkist." (510)

We all possess a great reservoir of culture and history. Denial of the right to dip into this reservoir leaves the soul parched with thirst: an uncouth, unkist spirit searching a barren desert.

WORKS CITED

The Oxford Dictionary of Quotations, Rev. Ed. (1955). London: Oxford University Press.

Wilde, Oscar. Preface to *The Picture of Dorian Gray* (1957). New York: Heritage Press.

On "Sonnets to Human Beings" by Carmen Tafolla

Rosaura Sánchez
University of California at San Diego

Discourses within Chicano literature have spanned a broad range of domains and historical periods. Since the decade of the 1970s in particular, these texts have often dealt with mythical constructs of *curanderismo* and *brujería*, with reconstructions of the arduous passage north across the Río Grande, the wire fence at the San Ysidro-Tijuana border or the deserts of the Southwest, with configurations of the perennial trip south in search of Mexican roots and identity, with traditional accounts of maturation linked to nostalgia for a lost past, with representations of exploitation in the fields and violence, alienation, acculturation and marginalization in urban sites, and with figurations of individual and collective subjectivity. More recently, to these networks of discourses, Chicana poets and fiction writers have added discourses of gender and sexuality, often articulated with those of ethnicity and class. Now, with the end of the century fast ahead, the direction of Chicano literature and more specifically the literature of Chicana women is a suggestive and open field.

Perhaps the latest work by Carmen Tafolla can provide some indication of future directions. In her collection of poems, "Sonnets to Human Beings," Tafolla offers a mapping of ethnic and class spaces that goes beyond national borders and configures them on a broad global scale even while continuing to make inroads into familiar territory with gender discourses of reproduction and ethnic discourses of acculturation. Although constructs of an indigenous past also continue to sediment the texts, and discourses of community and family serve still to generate a collective identity, there is also now an international and inter-ethnic subjectivity interpolated as much by discourses of oppression, exploitation and repression, as by discourses of frustration and quiet desperation. The poetry, as we will find, is marked in fact by a multiplicity of counter-discourses and a quest for ensuring collective identification through a refamiliarization of difference that is recognizable in the "Other" and made one's own.

The poem "In Guatemala" is a good example of counter-discourses and inter ethnic/international identification. It mocks the U.S. government's reassessment of political conditions in Guatemala as markedly improved in the midst of the slaughter of the indigenous population and the continued repression of labor organizers, peasants and Indian communities by the Guatemalan military. In Guatemala there are at present over 20,000 people living in "popular resistance communities" in two areas of El Quiché, in the Ixil Triangle and in the Ixcan jungle region. These displaced Quiché Indians are part of the more than 1.3 million peasants who fled between 1981-1982 to escape massacres perpetrated by the Guatemalan army (Edwards, 4). Those interested in providing assistance for refugees and the displaced have also had to face a hostile environment. In September 1991, anthropologist Myrna Mack, a Guatemalan researcher writing on the displaced, was stabbed to death in Guatemala City in an incident similar to those faced by human rights activists in El Salvador, Mexico, and other parts of Latin America. Tafolla's poem thus counters governmental U.S. whitewashing of its puppet governments in Latin America with graphic representations of the stark realities of political repression.

Tafolla's poem "In Guatemala" builds on discourses countering political violence in all its manifestations—torture, dismemberment, rape—as well as on constructs of resistance, specifically cultural resistance. The interconnection of these discourses allows for an unmasking of the rhetoric mouthed by political leaders who "scratch each other's backs" and with a laugh deny the existence of repression, while human heads roll. "There are no political prisoners here," the political figures attest, but in the background Indian heads lie trampled by government officers, "whole Indian villages [are] corralled, beheaded," and human hands and fingers reach out from the jungle floor crying for justice. The poem is a strong denunciation not only of the genocide in Guatemala but also of the hegemonic ideological discourses produced by the heads of state who justify the murders, disappearances, torture and devastation of indigenous areas in the name of democracy and humanitarianism. The poem allows us to recall that during the Reagan presidency the U.S. President informed Congress that the U.S. was supplying military equipment to Guatemala "to reinforce the improvement in the human rights situation" (Chomsky, 29). Clearly the U.S. government has been lending monetary support to mass murder and, as the poem puts it, to "non-justice."

But it is in her poem "Sweet Remember" that Tafolla's feminist and international positionings interconnect to provide counter-discourses for a powerful construct of feminine gender. Adopting an ironic tone, the poem is a "gentle" reminder to other women of the need to disarticulate romantic notions of girl and womanhood that portray the "fairer sex" as sweet innocent creatures who need the protective arms of men, in light of the torture and rape perpetrated against young and older women throughout the world. The poem reminds us of the many "disappeared" women, many raped with an electric prod by men who spread their legs "with great delight/to see [them] scream/till dead" and the many forced to hang by their knees "wrists tied to feet / till circulation ceased." The reality that "little girls" face is nothing like that promised by children's rhymes of sweetness and spice, for the young too are "immersed / in ice cold water" to force their mothers to betray their husbands' whereabouts. And to save their children, the mothers speak only to find themselves along with their daughters being torn up "right through the core / mass party rape in / stereo / and screams / galore." Researchers and survivors have documented thousands of cases of disappearances, torture, and genocide throughout the world, but particularly in Argentina, Uruguay, Chile, Guatemala, and El Salvador since the decade of the '60s, not only of those involved in political opposition but also of those related in any way, by blood, friendship, work or residence, to protestors or to those considered obstacles in maintaining a favorable climate for "free" enterprise. And of course, among these violated victims, many have been women. After reviewing a series of heinous acts against women, the poetic subject admonishes women to teach their daughters to be strong, as they will be on their own, to "face life straight / and stand on solid feet / and feel respect for [their] own being / temple, soul and head." In view of a world of violence against women it is time to stop the charade of teaching women to be "delicate" and "weak," "to always need a male escort / to think that only he protects." Although the poem does not explore why the world is not a safe haven for women directly, it does make clear that this is institutionalized violence against women and that the torture, rape and disembowelment is practiced by repressive governments. The poem also cautions women to beware of the pitfalls of complacency in a world where some have the "authority" to butcher and torture while others have "no guarantees in life." Being a "lady" thus offers no saving grace.

The world is indeed a rocky space straddled like the San Andreas Fault by a good portion of the world's population. In "Living on the San Andreas" the poet wonders "what / we are doing / here," "why there are so few poets / [. . .]criticizing the ends." In this world full of faults there is no New World Order, only a recycled version of the Old Order, with the Third World, as well as the destitute, the unemployed, the street people, and the working class within the First World, to be written off by a global Police Force and bombed into submission when any of those considered superfluous people dare to rock the boat. "How shall I tell you that I love you," asks the poet in another poem, when the world seems to offer no more than mass murder, human rights abuses, slaughter, torture, chemical and bacteriological warfare. In this text the poet begins to question the simple joys of companionship and love of nature in a topsy-turvy world bent on the destruction of the non-compliant.

From this global perspective the focus at times narrows and space becomes almost microscopic only to zoom away again, but now to a familiar public space, made intimate in its familiarity. It is now the place of the working class, the space of workers with a history. In "Ancient workers" it is a worker's hand that is on center stage, a hand with its lines "engraved / by the ancient workers," a hand in which the labor of forefathers is etched into the hand, each line a sign, a letter, a communicative trace, each worker alive in future generations, each individual the repository of these chipped marks, these lines of labor. From a genetic interpretation, the poem opens itself up to a historicized reading, to the construction of identity in terms of production and labor relations, links and tests that bind people and make them what they are.

In "Poquito allá" we step back to encompass in our sights the hand of one particular worker, a Chicano war veteran who survived the death and destruction of the war with every limb intact only to return home to the United States and lose two fingers and part of his hand at work. The "gringo," the boss, told him to "reach down in there" and "get that wrench" and then, impatient to leave the shop, "he flipped the switch too soon—ya casi era tiempo de salir." The doctors sewed one finger back onto the maimed hand but there was no compensation for his loss. In fact the boss "forgot to pay me for that day / or maybe scared to send the cash / for fear I'd ask for more."

This poem is also dialogical; only now instead of having the poet dialoguing with an absent interlocutor, it is the character within the poetic narrative that speaks out. The voice is clearly that of an older man, a good-natured grandfather who chuckles and converses with a stranger, a concerned stranger who inquires about his hand. Within his bilingual, code-switching explanation to his interlocutor he incorporates additional snippets of dialogue with his boss:

> "Los gringos sometimes, son así
> Se siente mal, because he was the one who said
> 'Reach down in there for me and get that wrench'
> and then he flipped the switch too soon—
> I'd worked for him all day, clean up, go home,
> and didn't wait to see that it was out."

The old man however is not bitter. Even without the full use of his hand he still feels productive. He can still plant for his wife, fix chairs, make chocolate, pick up the hen's eggs for his sisters, shake hands, hug, and hold up his toddler grandson with his good fingers. What matters to him and what makes his life retain value are not lost to him. An essential part of the dialogue is thus the discourse of family. His identity as part of a collectivity which includes his wife, his sisters and their grandchildren, and grandchildren of his own is what softens his resentment and allows him to view hazards at work as isolated incidents, accidents, which become ameliorated with time ("It doesn't bother me too much.") Family is thus constructed as a space of refuge and dominant over discourses of class and exploitation.

Family continues to be the dominant discourse in "Concha's Brother." Concha's brother is a loser, a drunkard, fast to start a fight, especially with gringo cops, write bad checks, cheat his clients, use and abuse women, joke and make "the best fajitas." But it is the fact that he is part of Concha's family that allows the narrator a degree of familiarity to note the loneliness fracturing his macho façade and his heartbreak over his first wife's leaving. In this poem and in "In love with people" the poetic voice provides fast takes on individuals in the barrio, each with a particular feature, a distinctive toss of the head, flicker of the eye, sweet smile, each with that little something that identifies those we love. These discourses are definitely maternal, forgiving, nurturing and caring and in sharp contrast with the voice of invective which denounces the slaughter of the indigenous population of Guatemala.

"La querencia del toro" offers a synthesis of a variety of discourses with its overview of life in the city. Once again a public space—the park —is familiarized and provided with a dint of intimacy. Here young and old inhabit their *querencia*, the spot in the arena where the bull makes his stand against the bullfighter, as wounded souls, not pierced physically like the bull, but afflicted economically and psychologically, yet willing to struggle on in a world that threatens to crush them. At the park the lame old man picks up empty aluminum cans to earn a few pennies while the nun is out reciting her prayers of self-denial. In the early morning, a middle-aged professional Chicano jogs to relieve his resentment, his sense of frustration with an incompetent boss, "puffing anger out and disappointment" to work out his concern over an unfavorable evaluation. The park is a metaphor for the barrio, the community itself that provides relief to the old and the young, as evident in the jogger's race down the hill: "his spirit healed by places / where defeat is honest." The owl he meets upon the hill—is it Última's spirit?—is linked in the final section to a child who steals away in anger to build her own "houses of moist mud under the house." The park itself is no longer present, only an empty lot nearby in the barrio where the houses have been torn down and the sun has bleached the discarded aluminum cans. The little girl's mud houses "may stay / for quite a while / Until the owl's children have landed / quietly / on blank-labeled cans." In areas subject to urban renewal, houses of the poor too often are razed or removed with the dwellers displaced from their *querencia*. The mud houses built by the girl with a stolen kitchen knife are thus only a momentary expression of defiance. By nightfall when the owlets descend upon the empty lot, they will have disappeared, but this child too will have learned to take a stand within the barrio, within her *querencia*, where she too must struggle and find peace, sometimes in "honest defeat" like the young professional. More than resignation, the poem points to the small, day-to-day struggles of every individual within the barrio and the need to move beyond defeat.

Tafolla's poetry is multi-valent. It combines discourses of violence, political repression, and feminine oppression with those of family, neighborhood, country and world in familiar and defamiliarized spaces. Its dialogical, bilingual and bidialectal discourses enable the poetic voice to be heteroglossic and to reconfigure a variety of perspectives. Tafolla's poetry opens up Chicana literature onto a wider discursive field and increased diversity.

References:

Edwards, Louise. "Guatemala. Vocies from Silent Refuge," in *NACLA*, vol. XXV, no. 1, July 1991, pp.4-5.

Chomsky, Noam. "Year 501: World Orders Old and New. Part I," in *Z Magazine*, March 1992, pp. 24-36.

"The mark of you is full of language": Language, Culture, and Scars in Carmen Tafolla's "Hot Line" and "In Memory of Richi"

Sandra Luz Pedregal

The mark of you is soft and bright on my body
    The ridge is smooth up my belly
        disruptedly even
        deep and rich in color
             and unforgettable

        like you.

"Hot Line" and "In Memory of Richi" are two disruptedly even poems in Carmen Tafolla's previously unpublished "Sonnets to Human Beings." So far apart they seem unlinked, two separate events, but in reality two poems that come together in a scar "like concentrated satin."

"Hot Line" can be described as a poem that both in its structure and topic represents a line that links the mother with her "firstborn, firstdead" child. Now that the child has died, the scar that marks the woman's body has become a "private red hot line" which keeps the memory of her daughter alive, thus replacing the once life-giving umbilical cord which linked daughter and mother. The scar through its written form, the poem, becomes the life-giving connection for the child. The breaks and links in the organization of the poem remind us of the broken and cut cord of life, and of the scar this break has left behind. A vertical scar has been created not only on the woman's body, but also on the page, a vertical line fading into nothingness, just like the scar it represents:

on this our own
    private

red

hot line

Unlike "Hot Line," "In Memory of Richi" starts somewhat faded, and as the poem progresses, it becomes jam packed with no room for breathing, no room to leave. This effect is so great that the lonely "Ritchie" at the end comes out as if fleeing from "the cell" Tafolla has created, a cell of time ("one day, six hours") and space ("a school," "a hall"). But this is not just a physical cell; the school becomes a trap the child must escape. From a place of growth and hope, it becomes a cultural trap in which Richi loses the most important things to an individual, his name, his culture, his identity, and there is no escape. When he "comes filtering down the hall," he has lost "the light and wealth" that once existed in his eyes. In six hours he has been taught the "error" of his ways.

Both poems, then, are linked by a sense of loss. A physical loss for the mother and a spiritual loss for Richi. In "Hot Line" although the physical loss of the child is painful, the mother finds comfort in her culture and her language. Her physical scar that will mark her for life is like "the aged viejita . . . had said" full of "voice and use and language," a language that keeps not only the memory of the child alive, but also the hope that one day they will be reunited, and there lies the importance of keeping in touch and hearing the message.

One cannot avoid thinking about the mothers in Patzcuaro who, on the night before All Saints' Day (el día de los muertos), make a link of flowers between their children's tomb and the parent's home, so the children can find their way home the next day, when they are invited to join the family again. This symbolism keeps the union alive, makes the difuntito part of the family once more; keeps the child from wandering in the world of the dead, identifies the child to his/her ancestors, so they will keep him/her until the time when the family, and in particular the mother, are together again with the child. The child becomes the link between the family and its ancestry, between the family and their heritage, their identity.

Similarly in "Hot Line," the mother has created a link between herself and her child, inviting the child to come to her each night, giving her message of love, keeping the union alive. But unlike the link between the mothers of Patzcuaro and their children, this one is not a path of flowers but a path/link of words. Language is, then, the cultural manifestation that permits and encourages the union of both, giving the mother not only a link to her ancestry, and as a result an identity, but doing the same for the child. This link, then, to a common ancestry through language is what identifies them, it is what unites them, it is what will always link them, even after death. The physical scar that marks the mother only becomes a concrete manifestation of this union and "Hot Line" its written form. The link/union is now eternal, written down for posterity, thanks to their language and to their culture.

In "In Memory of Richi" on the other hand, the loss is not a physical one, it is a spiritual one. The child survives. However, in a short time he has lost that which linked him to his ancestry: his name, a name that for six years has given him an identity, and with its loss, the link to his culture has been destroyed. The title, then, is quite appropriate. "Richi" has died. The process is not important, as Tafolla does not give us the details of how it happened. We do not even hear it from Richi himself, but from a teacher. What is important is the result: the loss of language, of culture, of identity. While in "Hot Line" the mother seeks comfort for the loss in her language, in "In Memory of Richi," the child is not permitted that comfort. His hopes of the promised knowledge and learning on that first day of school are denied and destroyed. In order to "succeed," he pays the price. The psychological scar is permanent. He loses all.

His is not a physical scar but a cultural scar that will mark him for life. The lonely "Ritchie" at the end and that firm "NO" denying not only his name but also his heritage emphasize the child's new life alone, without his ancestry, without his culture, without that "wealthy" and "deep in Spanish tones" language that would give him pride and confidence. His scar does not have "voz, virtud e idioma" It is dead, just like "his new eyes." As we can see, his mark is full of NOTHING.

The Pig's Eye View
Of Quality Literature

Beverly S. Rubin
Santa Monica College

What is quality literature? Does a prominent writer, such as Stephen King, lack quality solely because he/she has garnered a large following in the genre of popular literature? Conversely, should we consider an ancient book with obtuse meaning classic solely because of its antiquity? One person may discover a work to be "quality," while another may find the same work pretentious. What constitutes profound meaning to one individual may be fatuous to another. This dichotomy exists in the most lofty circles of literary academia. One individual cannot determine a conclusive yardstick for another.

Literature serves as an historical and cultural record, but it is also an art form. Relatability across diverse eras and cultures is only one literary guideline. Truly classic literature addresses a given human condition germane to all classes of individuals and social structures. We need not rely on academia to be the sole judge of literature: the voice of the multitudes should be the definitive factor. Academics should serve the people solely by analyzing "why" literature is loved.

Two twentieth century writers deserving of the title "quality" are Carmen Tafolla and Dorothy Parker. These individuals eradicate the sexist label of "women writers." They speak to the soul of contemporary issues with remarkable, lyrical poetry. The reader enjoys these writers on their own merit and leaves behind tiresome comparisons of gender or ethnic background.

"Quality Literature" (Tafolla 25-26) provides a thought-provoking analysis of the determination of "quality." This prosodic story — with its absorbing blend of pathos and delight — considers the contention that it is to one's advantage to read lesser-known authors who tend to be ignored, but are undeniably worthy of note. Tafolla's writing solidly attacks the Western Eurocentric bias evident in many college literature courses.

Here, we meet a Chicano student and his elitist professor, Dr. Dumont. The student informs the teacher that he has chosen a Chicana author. The professor, having never heard of the writer, simply dismisses the student by saying, "Chicano literature simply isn't *quality*." Dumont emphatically repeats his assertion throughout the story. The student vainly attempts to make his point: "But this stuff's good! I mean, it's the first stuff . . . that really talks about real things." The student is able to relate to the work and demonstrates his conviction and courage in challenging his teacher's "educated" dismissal.

The professor endeavors to "help" his pupil, stating '[T]here simply hasn't *been* any quality Chicano literature. If you *must* [emphasis added] have something in Spanish, try Darío . . . or Cervantes . . . Darío has been highly acclaimed in Madrid, and even Paris." As the professor continues his dissent, the student asks him to consider other Mexican-American authors. It is at this point that Dumont realizes that the student had received a "very poor mark" on the last examination and decides that there is no point in continuing the discussion. "[I]t hasn't even been critiqued in the PMLA, and until it has been critiqued in the PMLA, I can't say it's quality literature!" The professor clearly perpetuates the emphasis on Western European literature through his own inability to conduct judgment independently of a defined authority. We ask ourselves who should be receiving "very poor marks."

"Quality Literature" is a scathing indictment of the close-minded snobbery of the Dr. Dumonts on college campuses. The professor is unwilling to continue to learn from writers outside the traditional literary aristocracy — a dangerous practice for an educator. He lacks humility and the devouring thirst for knowledge. His smug complacency, and his disinclination to explore the richness of text and poetry from cultures foreign to his own narrow realm within the collegiate caste system isolate him from being a good judge of quality. This is the type of individual who cannot take the risk of exposing his colleagues to new forms of classic literature: an attitude at odds with his profession.

Dumont's crystallized attitude is evident. Indeed, he is too ignorant to discern the difference between the Mexican-American and Spanish cultures. Even his "crisp, pseudo-British accent" gives the reader pause — we immediately find him affected. His continued tirade of what constitutes "quality" literature throughout this story fortifies our initial impression. Tafolla's point hits the mark when she ends her story with a satirical epithet. '[T]he professor walked off into a semi-colon . . . as the face of the student became an epic poem."

The teacher's fossilized outlook (a possible reflection on the grave peril in which the American educational system finds itself today) makes it difficult for non-European heritage students to relate to Eurocentric literature. Let's reverse this example. A student well-versed in the works of Shakespeare and other European literature may find the subtle shades of Eastern philosophy embodied in Confucius' *Analects* ambiguous and confusing; however, most Confucius scholars agree that the examination of this venerable author is paramount to the understanding of Chinese culture and history.

To ignore an author's work because we lack knowledge of his culture means our understanding of others is limited. In the modern world, it is paramount that we take time and appreciate other cultures if we are to live peacefully. We do ourselves a grave disservice by dis- missing the literature of any culture. This is particularly true of Chicano literature. The ethnicity of Mexico, a nation with which we share a border and history, has a major impact on Chicano/Chicana literature. We effectively annihilate a major segment of the heritage of the United States by not expanding our horizons to include

Chicano literature.

Dorothy Parker, an acclaimed author of her time, also uses satire to convey her disdain of what is considered "quality" literature. Of her education, she stated, "high schools don't teach you how to read" (Keats 20). "A Pig's Eye View of Literature" (Portable Dorothy Parker 219-22) is a collection of four-line stanzas about the work of various authors. Parker uses her inimitably snide style to courageously take issue with so-called "quality" writers who have been deified in literary circles. Some excerpts from her quatranic satire are:

Alfred, Lord Tennyson

Should Heaven send me any son,
    I hope he's not like Tennyson.
    I'd rather have him play a fiddle
    Than rise and bow and speak an idyll.

Alexandre Dumas and His Son

Although I work, and seldom cease,
    At Dumas *pére* and Dumas *fils*,
    Alas I cannot make me care
    For Dumas *fils* and Dumas *pére*

Dorothy Parker expresses her ire at "snob-appeal" poetics in caustic sentiments towards pompous and arrogant authors who refuse to be relatable to the reader. Another "Parkerism" reads:

Walter Savage Landor

Upon the work of Walter Landor
    I am unfit to write with candor.
    If you can read it, well and good;
    But as for me, I never could.

Parker's courage in challenging the status quo is refreshing and reaffirms that, if a work cannot be understood by the populace, it is not quality.

Unfortunately, some scholars and professors go to great lengths to exhibit their lofty knowledge to "talk down" to their audience by making a point of using obtuse terminology. Since writing is a communicative art, the lack of relatability benefits no one.

A problematic image arises in ascertaining "quality" literature in the practice of endless textual analysis. While it is true that a scan of poetic form is valuable in terms of understanding an author's work, "over-analysis" diminishes enjoyment and turns people away from aspiring to read. When a vast majority of readers are diverted from the joy of reading, the necessity of analysis is questionable. Analysis fails when it does not achieve communal reach.

A case in point is a volum.nous work of approximately three hundred pages on the epic *Beowulf*, which deals specifically with rhyme and meter techniques as utilized by the poem. The book scrutinizes each word of the epic, fitting the entire work into endless charts. This pontification neglects the epic's heroic theme and results in a useless tool for comprehension. This book is more ideally suited to a calculus class: its focus on formulae is similar to that encountered in solving equations of several variables. After three pages of this book, one forgets the epic's heroic and heart-stirring ambience. Analysis of art has its place; however, the desire to appreciate artistic beauty first-hand is the quintessence of understanding.

Romantic poetry was food for the medieval soul, but satirical poesy and short stories are more satisfying fare to avid readers of contemporary literature. Popular satirical topics elucidate the modern soul through relatability to character development and plot. We appreciate satire as a means by to gain understanding of our individual processes of emotional and mental maturity.

Early epics, such as *The Odyssey, Oedipus Rex,* and *Antigone* brim with irony, and Chaucer, in his *Canterbury Tales,* is redolent with ribald humor that pokes fun at the "characters" of his era. However, with the introduction of the Shakespearean sonnets, the use of satire in poetry was eclipsed by romance. During the Elizabethan era, certain scholars became static in their convictions that "good" poetry was either romantic or religious, giving rise to divergent conceptions of quality literature.

Dorothy Parker's writings are powerfully sarcastic. Parker's work is not for the faint-hearted reader of vapid romance novels. Her acerbicism eclipses the vision of a rose-colored world. Her sentiments are shocking, refreshing, and amusing:

Resumé

Razors pain you;
   Rivers are damp;
   Acids stain you;
   And drugs cause cramp.
   Guns aren't lawful;
   Nooses give;
   Gas smells awful;
   You might as well live. (61)

We do not find interminable, flowery outpourings of undying declarations of unrequited love in Parker. She conveys volumes of emotion in compacted, acid sentiments. When Parker lends her technique of streamlined satire to a topic such as suicide, the unthinkable becomes amusing. "Resumé" is relatable. We perceive that someone else has battled the shadowy and enigmatic side of consciousness. Here, satire teaches us that we are not alone in our feelings.

Carmen Tafolla, too, neatly encompasses the satirical in her poetry. In "To Mr. Gabacho Macho," she eloquently expresses the reality of prejudice:

And you're *sure* this isn't Pleasantville

or Smithville U.S.A.
Or Tom, Betty, and Susan's home
or even "Happy Days." [. . .]

There's hunger here and anger too,
and insult and frustration. [. . .]

Our men head more than welfare lines
And our women aren't so timid [. . .]

The only sombreros I ever saw
were on the heads of tourists

Tafolla and Parker convey their satire in dissimilar styles. However, both elucidate the irony of the human condition. Parker uses her journalistic background to deliver sparse jabs of venomous verbiage, coloring her words with cosmopolitan seasoning. Tafolla's words beckon us to a lush, fertile forest, but the destination is initially unclear. The reader relates to both the fatalism in "Resumé" and the anger in "To Mr. Gabacho Macho." Satire coerces us to take inventory of our feelings, teaching us to laugh at ourselves and forgive ourselves for our shortcomings.

The interminable poetic discourse regarding love — particularly the unrequited variety — has been overdone. This is an area where satire serves to keep us from unfulfilled yearning. The subject of love in verse has become a comic parody. In our modern society, we find Elizabeth Barrett Browning's work less relevant than that of satirical realists such as Parker and Tafolla. We may appreciate Browning's tremendous talent, but her writing is remote. Parker's writing hits closer to the experience of love in contemporary society. She cautions us against maudlin sentimentality by the use of catch quatrains to succinctly state, "Just deal with it!" For example,

Some men break your heart in two,
    Some men fawn and flatter,
Some men never look at you,
    And that cleans up the matter. (118)

This taut stanza speaks without encyclopedias.

Although more loquacious, Carmen Tafolla also invites us to "deal with it" and grow as individuals as she refrains from proselytizing. For example, Tafolla uses an interesting analogy in the poem, "in the wash." The words flow together simply and eloquently. Tafolla recalls fragments of phrases from a failed relationship, as her intellectual side discovers, "but that wasn't it." She asks, "What *is* it?"

When she "(finally)" wearies of the nonsense, she scathingly and satirically observes the man's weakness. She now sees his faults clearly, and successfully joins the themes of blind passion at the beginning of "in the wash" and ultimate realization at its conclusion. The diachronic sequence of Tafolla's words follows the same sequence of her relationship. At the beginning of the poem, she feels a need to chase after someone who does not support her emotional depth and intellectual accomplishments. The man's fear of virginity is chronicled by Tafolla: "Any woman could have told you / that blood comes out in the wash / though not easily."

The emotional genesis at the end of the poem shows us that she has seen what a coward her ex-lover is ("[. . .] unlike that first spot / of blood / that frightened you so"). "In the wash" encourages us to question why we fear our feelings. Tafolla instructs us that, although our emotions may bleed when we are rejected, we can rise above our fears of a relationship, especially when we focus on the example of her ex-lover, who is afraid of growth, who became an object of ridicule.

Ultimately, Tafolla writes about her own cleansing. She washes away the mire of emotional ties so she can rise above feelings that are not fitting. The image of blood is particularly telling. Although it was not washed out of her soul easily, the blood eventually came out "in the wash." Tafolla was able to transcend her pain. We understand the process of awareness when we read, "as you glanced nervously / at my ring finger / to see if someone had / 'purchased' my allegiance." Tafolla "(finally)" becomes aware of the "covered-up excuses" and "lack of" love, finding the strength to extricate herself from a negative situation: a situation to which we can relate.

The term "quality" as it applies to "literature" is up to each of our individual conceptions. There are innumerable ways to judge why we are partial to particular works. Whether we consider irony, detailed analysis, meter, plot scrutiny, or other criteria, there is no irrefutable criterion. Our duty-bound journey is to explore various kingdoms of reading in our own heroic voyages, improving our ability to recognize "quality" literature. We can then decide with specificity those works that have engraved in our souls the remembrance that determines "quality literature."

WORKS CITED

Tafolla, Carmen. *Curandera*. Santa Monica: Lalo Press, 1983.

Keats, John. *The Life and Times of Dorothy Parker*. New York: Simon & Schuster, 1970.

Parker, Dorothy. *The Portable Dorothy Parker*. New York: Viking Press, 3rd Printing, 1974.

Parker, Dorothy. *Enough Rope*. New York: Pocket Books, 1939.

Carmen Tafolla's Poetry:
Private Experience, Public Voice

Joel Pérez
San Diego Mesa College

In 1987 (has it been that long already?), as a graduate student at the University of California, Riverside, I had the pleasure of listening to Carmen Tafolla read from her work during "Writers Week." I became curious that this young Chicana poet, tan güera, could relate experiences so revelatory of Chicano life yet, at the same time, touch upon the universal aspects of human experience.

In a subsequent interview for the local Chicano student paper, she explained how her culture has deeply influenced her poetic efforts because the values she writes about "come from the people I know, the experiences I have had, and the clash of cultures and the tensions which arise from the meeting of two ways of looking at the world." Not surprisingly, the poet creates her images and ideas through that language learned within the family and the culture, a language which her father taught her could be magical and playful. Indeed, Tafolla's poetry consistently upholds the culture and values of her people (voiceless for so long in the literature of her country) and transcends the group's personal experience to reach universal dimensions that connect to all human life. Thus, her work exhibits a sensitive humanistic attitude that has the potential to touch all readers. Tafolla's poetry, then, speaks of private experiences, but becomes a public utterance for a/all people and a/all culture(s).

Tafolla learned early about the magic of words and how potent language could be from her father, who liked to alter and create variations of songs: "Santa Claus es coming soon, en su guang-guilón." This example synthesizes the bilingual aspects of Tafolla's familial and cultural experience, and shows, too, her father's ability to invent and use playful satire.

But Tafolla apparently also made a conscious decision to write what she wanted and how she wanted despite the critics' advice to "write in one language," for there is much to write about: familia, weeds that crawl "over sidewalks pa' juntarse," and "Mexican gardens and backyards" ("Right in One Language").

Little wonder, then, that Tafolla exploits these aspects of language to render vivid images in her poetry. The portrait of a favorite relative (the black sheep) in "Tía Sofía" emerges sharply drawn in flashback through words that lovingly but accurately describe her:

> She sings to pass the time
> "Ah foun' mah three-uhl
> own Blueberry Hee-uhl."

[. . .]

Tía Sofía speaks Tex-Mex
with Black English
and *all* the latest slang.

Not being like the other daughters in the family, Tía Sofía had not attended church regularly, not been a stay-at-home kind. Therefore, her "lack of piety" and non-conformist attitude had embarassed her family, who, when she died,

Didn't feel quite right saying
"She's always been a good Christian."
So they praised the way
"siempre se arreglaba la cara,"
"se cuidaba,"

The speaker's sympathy for Tía Sofía carries within it a satirical poke at the other family members, especially the sisters, who try to speak kindly about her, but only after her death. The satisfying resolution of the poem comes at the funeral, when the speaker appropriately feels like laughing and singing in a Black Tex-Mex as Tía Sofía used to do, in the words that still retain her image in memory.

Tafolla uses language, too, that clearly demonstrates the mixing of two cultures and modes of thinking. Jack Sullivan, in an article written for *Hispanic Link,* has called it a Contact Vernacular, a new language created by the Mexican-American. In "Los Corts 2. (el chamaquito)," we find some examples of this new linguistic creation. A boy finds some money and happily ponders how he will spend it: "¡Jiiiii-jo! ¡Me jayé un *daime*! / ¡Ta hueno eso! / Pa los airplanes que venden de wood / (¿O eran de *cuara* esos? / Nuimporta — hasta los beisból carts se compran a *nicle*." I have italicized the words that clearly represent new linguistic coinages (no pun intended). Two other aspects stand out as well: the bilingual quality and the common mispronounciation and contraction of Spanish words. This language, according to Sullivan, "goes beyond a dialect of Spanish; it is unintelligible to native speakers of Spanish." But it represents the language of an entire group, the words that Tafolla grew up hearing in the family circle and in the neighborhood.

The language in Tafolla's poetry, being a product of culture, has a double effect. It upholds the culture and its values, and also transcends specific linguistic, cultural, and nationalistic boundaries. "Poquito Allá," a more recent poem, presents a portrait of a Mexican auto mechanic who has lost some fingers in an accident through the carelessness of his gringo boss. The Mexican blames no one, accepting the accident as part of God's larger plan. After all, he had been through a war with no injuries and he still has so much. He can still plant roses and cilantro and make "*chocolate,* stirring strong." His former boss, however, who "always was uncomfortable with Mexicans," still feels so bad that he will avoid meeting the mechanic in public. The latter thinks that it is "[t]oo bad it bothers him so much. / I still do all I used to 'cept for / playing the guitar and carving wood." In fact, the loss of a few fingers serves to emphasize what is of real worth in the life of this man. His maimed hand can still "saludar, shake hands, y abrazar," and his good fingers can guide his little grandson to stand upright, "Derecho, fuerte, unafraid / Poquito aquí, poquito allá. . . ."

Similarly, other poems demonstrate the poet's sensibility toward and admiration of her people and culture, as in "¡Ahay!" where "A hearty laugh rumbles / and un grito mexicano — ¡Ajay! / . . . / Sinvergüenza smile dances in to say / "Qué raza tan más bonita" / . . . / And his singing voice / refuses to know the meaning / of defeat."

Ultimately, the family for Tafolla represents the heart, the soul, the center of individual and communal experience. This center nurtures the body ("corn is ground," "to make tamales" on "a stone comal") and nourishes the spirit ("supper tables feel the pulse of human hands / and breathe it back to them, with blessings"). The concept of family, this place, symbolically expands to become more inclusive and accepting of all life, for "even zopilotes have a softness to their name." Consequently, Tafolla's poetry reaches out to all readers and attempts to bring them to the harboring arms of the family, where "There is a place / hay un lugar / donde hay un lugar para tí."

Tafolla's humanism necessarily compels her to treat all people as part of the larger human family. And so, the title of the award-winning manuscript, "Sonnets to Human Beings," seems quite natural. In addition, it seems quite proper that the subject matter of some of the poems should be about being "In Love With People," or about how our humanity connects us all:

In that cold-windowed house
        lies a woman
    old and silent with large roving eyes
    bare beneath her clothes in a shrunken frame,
        and thin as onionskin over bones.

[. . .]

I lean over the still body, still mattress-bound,
    and wonder who she is and why I care
        so much.

In that tall-ceilinged ancient eight-walled house
    owned by cold drafts and volcanic spaces
I breathe in through her onionskin lungs
        and know,
    with her eyes too old to need vision to see
        that she
            is
            me.

("ancient house")

In a real sense, boundaries do not exist for Tafolla, the human being and poet. She writes of love, pain, delight, and sadness. She also writes about injustice and inhumanity, for what happens to one of us, happens to all of us, what implicates one, implicates all. The graphic images of "In Guatemala," for example, convince us that both those who engage in human injustice and those who pretend not to see it deserve condemnation. Euphemisms such as "political prisoners" cannot hide the horrors of men's heads being sewed "into the now-pregnant" bellies / of their fiancée's corpses." The poetic voice makes certain that the readers see the hypocrisy that hides behind convenient alliances and partnerships:

> There are only Presidents
> who scratch each other's backs,
> blindfold each other's eyes,
> laugh uncomfortably,
>
> [. . .]
>
> cutting too-human heads
> from the non-human bodies
> of non-justice.
>
> ("In Guatemala")

Here, the speaker clearly expresses a sense of outrage and horror at the inhumanity that too often passes for political convenience and opportunism. In this manner, Tafolla connects us all to universal themes and types of experiences.

Carmen Tafolla is a keen observer of human action. To communicate her impressions, she uses a linguistic utterance that comes from her father, family, and culture, a new language that allows her the freedom to express a full range of emotions and experiences. Tafolla writes mostly about her culture and people, but, because of her sensitive nature and humanism, her poetry over-flows the boundaries of the self to make universal statements. Therefore, her private voice has become a public discourse.

Naming the Mother in the Poetry of Carmen Tafolla

Dorothy S. Schmidt
The University of Texas-Pan American

"With Our Very Own Names" is the title of a live performance and reading that Carmen Tafolla presents across the United States. In the theatrical medley of selections, many of them found in this volume, a ritual of naming proceeds in almost totemic fashion as myriad characters claim their names and identities, or are claimed by them, in poignant dramatizations. Drawing from a family heritage that includes *curanderas* as well as Bible ministers, Tafolla explores the influences upon her own life as a Chicana, a writer, a feminist, and a professional. In doing so, she names objects, places, people, and events in a manner not merely personal, ethnic, or genetic, but one that transcends cultures, times, and places while she remains firmly grounded in her traditions.

In a sense, Tafolla's works might be labelled "confessional," since the persona of the poems is most often the poet herself. But "connectional" is a more appropriate description, for through this more immediate voice, the reader can hear the authenticity of the emotion or the experience. This extends the resulting insights to the lives of all who seek both personal and cultural identity from clues of lineage, behavior, and belief.

In some ways, this collection is reminiscent of N. Scott Momaday's memoir, *The Names* (Harper 1976), wherein his own naming is performed first by an old Indian doctor writing on the birth certificate (42), altered later by bureaucrats in some Indian Affairs office, and finally augmented and affirmed by his great-grandfather's giving him his first Indian name, Tsaoi-talee (57). In his preface, Momaday writes:

> My name is Tsaoi-talee. I am, therefore, Tsaoi-talee; therefore I am.
> The storyteller, Pohdlohk gave me the name Tsaoi-talee. He believed that a man's life proceeds from his name, in the way that a river proceeds from its source. (i)

Searching through the names of his ancestors enables Momaday to feel the connection, to understand his heritage, and to embrace it in all its dimensions.

For Tafolla, the remembrances of the people of her past, whether actual or fictional composites, also become her source, and their tracings in her present permeate her understanding of self. In the poem, "Nací La Hija," Tafolla recounts her lineage from one grandmother who was a *curandera*, a healer, and a grandfather who was a blacksmith. The other set of grandparents included a gardener-herbalist grandmother and a preacher grandfather. In the poem, she asks, "is it any wonder then" that she frequently finds herself forging remedies, preaching to plants, or trying to cure metal.

This acknowledgement of the diverse elements in the heritage of every Hispanic child is enhanced by Tafolla's use of both English and Spanish. Yet where Momaday in *The Names* seems comfortable with the cultural dimensions of his Anglo-Indian bloodlines, and the simplification (Anglicizing?) of his Indian name — Mammedaty to Momaday — Tafolla unflinchingly spotlights the tensions set up by concurrent adoption and rejection by Hispanics of various elements in the dominant culture.

Awareness of this ethnic dichotomy underlies most of Tafolla's work. Some of her earlier poems are polemic, acerbic in the identification of injustices inflicted by either bigoted or unthinking members of Anglo culture, but Tafolla's attacks are rapier-like or sardonically-witty, rather than sledgehammer blows or shotgun blasts. In many of the later poems, e.g., *Sonnets to Human Beings*, she seems intent on erasing national and cultural barriers to touch the core of shared human experience. Indeed, careful reading of the earlier works reveals an underlying assumption that, indeed, within this universal human experience, only the names have been changed.

Like Momaday, Tafolla acknowledges the importance of names to the understanding and development of the self. For Tafolla, the difference between the Hispanic, private, "owned" name and the Anglicized public name is a psychic split wherein the self can be bruised and denied. Just as the totemic name of a Native American is bestowed by an elder of the tribe, the natal name of the Mexican-American child is chosen for both personal meaning and ethnic custom. Yet these names in public become distorted and misunderstood, as in the poem, "Occupation: None," when the bewildered survey-taker cannot make "Maria Francisca Baca Gonzalez Montoya de Luján" fit in the official space provided for firstname, lastname, middle initial. Or in "Fighting Paper," when the bureaucracy cannot acknowledge the possibility of having *two* first names. In the poem, "In Memory of Richi," on the first day of school, a young Anglo teacher meets "Richi" in the hall, and is willing to be instructed in the correct pronunciation of his name. When they meet again, after the boy has attended other classes with other teachers, it is only to discover that in one short day of school, the Chicano child has become convinced of the total error of both his name and himself.

According to Judeo-Christian and Native American traditions, as well as other creation stories, humans are called upon to name not only themselves and their offspring, but all the creatures and objects that they encounter. In Tafolla's work, this naming becomes an erratic pendulum swinging between two languages and two cultures, yet unerringly faithful to the rhythms and idioms of each, and to their mestizo linguistic offspring, Tex-Mex or Spanglish. The phonetic spellings of English words are sometimes unfamiliar until pronounced, but the unerring accuracy of Tafolla's ear creates the musical "switching" prevalent in the Southwest.

In this process of naming, however, one name is so commonplace that it transcends languages and cultures. Every person alive recognizes it, yet under Tafolla's shaman-like touch, this name becomes mystical and magical in ways that strangely do not war with her firm feminism. Deeply embedded within many of these poems are the mothers — whose names we all say, yet seldom understand beyond the formality of designation. Tafolla traces the meanings and manifestations of motherhood from matriarchal *curanderas* to *tías* surrogating as *madres*, and from there to the bittersweet mysteries of being a mother to children both living and dead. And finally, she examines the maligned *La Malinche*, who becomes the mother not only of the Spaniard's child, but also, symbolically, of the New World itself.

As purveyors of knowledge and culture, mothers are the child's first teacher; this role is highlighted in works like the children's story, "Tacho, El Baby Tacuache," in which Mother Possum begins the instruction of her budding offspring when "Tacho" attempts to decorate the walls of her pouch. She instructs him not to draw on walls. When Tacho persists in his attempts to draw on various large blank surfaces, he continues to receive reinforcement of his mother's teaching until, finally, his need to draw on walls is recognized and he becomes a renowned mural artist. The instruction of the story is not just the demonstration of the Mother Possum character, but also is a lesson in a mother's effective redirection of a child's natural drives without destroying innate talents or a sense of self-worth. Thus, in Russian doll fashion, Tafolla nests the mother-teacher within the story, even as she, the mother-teacher-writer, fulfills that role through the story itself.

More direct instruction is contained in the poem "marked." The usual instrument given to a child learning to write is a pencil, but this mother-voice warns, "Never write with pencil, / m'ija. / It is for those / who would / erase." Instead, from ominous observation of the world and what it does to the indecisive, this mother encourages:

> Write with ink
>   or mud,
> or berries grown in
> gardens never owned,
>   or, sometimes,
>   if necessary,
>   blood.

Underscored in the poem "Sweet Remember" is the importance of "right teaching," the new things girl-children must know for survival in an increasingly violent world. Here, Tafolla shatters a catalog of traditional sweet and passive male-dependent behaviors for girls with a litany of atrocities committed against innocent women victims whose upbringing had not prepared them to fight back. And the poet admonishes, "this is why / I do not ask / my child to cry / to sit sweet helpless and be cute / . . . / to think herself so delicate / so weak[.]" Instead, Tafolla urges a strong self-reliance as the only defense:

> [. . .] that the bravest thing of all

to think, to feel, to care, and to recall
is to be human
and to be complete
and face life straight
and stand on solid feet
and feel respect for her own being
temple, soul, and head
and
that she owns her strong brave life
till dead

Respect for the mother-worker is apparent in many of the works. When the survey-taker in "Occupation: None" insists that this is the correct answer according to the instructions, Tafolla's María indignantly elaborates the reasons "none" is a false and ridiculous answer:

Yo me levanté a las cinco de la mañana —
cada mañanita de mi vida — a veces más temprano —
y que a hacer las tortillas, moler el chile, dar de comer
a los hombres, a los niños, a los amigos, a todos!
Y limpiar, y lavar, y enseñar a los hijos —
que whas right . . . y whas wrong . . .

And, in another poem, in a softer voice, Tafolla reassures herself and the reader that there is a place, "hay un lugar," where the sacrificial nature of such labors is appreciated, where "corn is ground by daily arms / and old metate smoothed by flow of family / . . . / and each plate is prepared / and carved to fit the tastes / for that one mouth."

In "Work Clothes," the connection is made between the parent's generation and the poet's through the clothes worn while performing each day's labor. The sturdiness of the parent's work attire — the mother's housedress spotted by bleach, its bosom worn by heavy heads and teary young cheeks; the father's heavy-duty pants and shoes that withstand weather, paint, soil — at first intimidates the writer who can find no comparable durability in her own closet. Then comes the realization that the cuff-frayed and ink-stained professional suit worn through too many conferences is the same, that "the story shining through the spots / . . . / I can hear it singing / a good day's work ahead."

Not all of the mothers named in the poems are revered and respected. In the "Los Corts" poem cycle about tenants in a low income housing development, two of the sections deal with mothers whose lives seem somewhat futile. In "Los Corts 1. (la madre)," the mother was a teenaged unwed mother, who now sits through heat-filled San Antonio afternoons, remembering her own lost beauty and yet sadly knowing that her daughter is growing up following the same patterns of directionless existence; even the cats under the corner streetlight seem to be the same old cats. In another of the apartments, an old woman, *"la viejita,"* is alone, though she has numerous offspring. Yet, in true martyr fashion, she excuses them and assuages her loneliness with photographs. The resignation and fatalism of these two maternal images is depressingly real.

The experience of fecundity itself is also more tragic than triumphant in some of these poems. In "Sweet Remember," pregnant women seem to be special targets of official and unofficial brutality. And fertility becomes the victim of cruel barter in "Nine Moons Dark," where a Mexican Indian mother gives birth to a healthy infant that is sold. Told that her child is dead, she is handed a chill gray baby corpse kept on hand for such contingencies. Similar loss echoes in the pain of "Scars and Three Daughters," wherein the poet explores the need for scars to remind us of where we have been, of "history unveiled," even when one of those scars is a constant heart-wrenching reminder of a stillborn child. Yet the mother comes to understand that neither can she, nor should she, attempt to protect the living daughter from having her own destiny recorded in the markings on her body; these will be her evidence of having lived. The personal loss of Tafolla's own firstborn, Cielos, represented by a telltale Cesarean scar, is further explored in "Hot Line," where the scar becomes the connection between the earthbound mother and the lost child. Yet the personal becomes the poetic as the writer states, "This mark of you on me / is full / of language / . . . / Each night I can reach down and feel it, / listen, / hear your message / . . . ."

Moving into an even more metaphysical contemplation of motherhood, "They Come From Within Us," Tafolla finds "deep in our untainted hideaways / in the fifth womb / of the fifth soul," "unwhispered," "unbirthed spiritchildren." Blooming in "tiny half-buds," these spiritchildren "blend into our blood," then leave, leaving behind traces and glimpses of beings other than the self. Then, in a rare switch of perception, the poet becomes the impregnator in "Fighting Paper":

Still
    I fight you
    daily courtesan who will not

        quit

    for all I want to do

    with you, papel,

    is take you

    fresh and peaceful,

    clean, of morning,

        full of past
    and new, like earthy present,

    to plow softly into you,

                    furrows of crumbling
                        readiness

            plant the words gently in your warmth

                    so that you might

                        — at last —

                        bear

                        fruit.

So there it is, poetry as the ultimate manifestation of symbolic motherhood, the powerful spirit-mother becoming capable of self-impregnation in
the act of the poem. And then, moving from the spiritchildren in the mystical
"fifth womb / of the fifth soul" to the poem, "woman-hole," Tafolla finds
powerful symbolism in:

[that] black hole —
        in the center of womanhood
            that swallows countless
                secrets and has strange
                    powers

The poet voice disclaims understanding why this is so, but affirms the
"black echo is music / is sister of sunlight / and from it / crece / vida." Thus in
Tafolla's poetry, as it is in much women's poetry, the womb is the symbol of this
genesis, this power of every woman to be reborn herself, as she bears life.

Even more symbolic of Tafolla's respect for this mystery, this female
power, is her portrait of *La Malinche*, the Cuauhtemoc princess who is
portrayed as the betrayer of her own people, even her own brother, because of
her love for Cortés, the Spaniard. She was labelled *"Chingada"* because the
people could not imagine she would aid the "enemy" in this fashion unless she
had been raped or seduced. In this apologia for those actions, Tafolla claims
that *La Malinche* was less victim than visionary:

I saw our world
        And I saw yours
            And I saw —
                another.

[. . .]

        a world yet to be born.
And our child was born. . .

[. . .]

        I saw a dream
            and I reached it.
                Another world...

La raza.

la raaaaaaaa-zaaaaa. . .

So, from the disgraced Indian mother came the proud mestizo heritage, the heritage that Tafolla affirms throughout these works. According to Gloria Anzaldua, writing in *Borderlands/La Frontera* (1987), "*La Cultura Chicana* identifies with the mother (Indian) rather than with the father (Spanish)." Tafolla emphasizes this relationship with *La Malinche's* charge against the Spaniard:

> Years later, you took away my child
> (my sweet mestizo new world child)
>   to raise him in your world.
> You still didn't see
>   You *still* didn't see.
> And history would call *me*
>   chingada.

In her introduction to *Woman of Her Word: Hispanic Women Write,* Evangelina Vigil writes, ". . . most importantly she[the woman] is the giver of life. Consequently she knows pain: the pain of giving birth, the pain of losing a child, the pain of seeing her children suffer, the pain of isolation and alienation" (7). Thus, in the poem "MotherMother," Tafolla makes a final, cosmic naming of the Earth itself. Occasioned by thoughts of the irony of nuclear weapons being spoken of as "defense," weapons such as the atomic bomb that demolished Hiroshima, the poem unites the personal and the public. Identifying Earth as a mother, who through that terrible act of annihilation has lost her child, her children, Tafolla claims this sisterhood of suffering — herself, her mother, all mothers:

> Your womb has been
>
>   cut open
>
>   just as mine
>   just as my mother's
>
> Your child has died
>
>   in its halo of innocence
>
>   just as mine
>   just as my mother's

Despite the losses — of innocence, of hope, of identity — suffered by all the children, all the mothers, the poem ends on a note of hope, of new birth, of regeneration:

Now —

  That child is gone
   That cut is mended

   But let us

    save

    the next.

Invoking the name of "mother" can be the most commonplace of stereo-types, but in many of the poems of Carmen Tafolla, this naming is personal, passionate, and provocative. Despite the varying intensity of these maternal portrayals, overall they represent a thematic core, a threshold from which her work encounters a broader audience. And from the naming emerges a human bonding that transcends language and cultural barriers to become universal.

WORKS CITED

Anzaldua, Gloria. *Borderlands/La Frontera.* Aunt Lute Press, 1987.

Momaday, N. Scott. *The Names.* New York: Harper, 1976.

Vigil, Evangelina. *Woman of Her Word: Hispanic Women Write.* Houston: Arte Público, 1983.

Carmen Tafolla:
An Observer Within

Bryce Milligan

One of several Chicana poets active in and around San Antonio, Texas, during the late 1960s and early 1970s, Carmen Tafolla emerged in the 1980s as one of the few truly gifted survivors. Multitalented, she is a respected educator and administrator, a cultural commentator with a biting wit, an accomplished short story writer, a sensitive and often hilarious children's author, and a poet — whose work this volume celebrates and expands.

Tafolla was born in 1951 in a westside San Antonio barrio where she attended public schools — including the somewhat infamous Rhodes Junior School, which is the subject of the lovingly bitter poem entitled "and when i dream dreams. . ." She received a four-year scholarship to attend high school at Keystone, a private institution for gifted students. Here, she learned that her beloved home barrio was not seen by all in the same light. This initial encounter with fear born out of cultural ignorance prompted the prose poem "Quality Literature"; it also partially inspired Tafolla's life-long work in support of multicultural education and understanding.

Tafolla's natural poetic idiom derives from her roots in westside San Antonio, a neighborhood steeped in tradition, poverty, and Catholicism — the richest sort of cultural loam. Yet the poet's earliest stimulus to write may, in fact, have been her isolation from that community. In her unpublished essay, "I was a Barrio Protestant," Tafolla describes how at age seven she discovered that her friends occasionally spoke a different language full of mysterious terms like "First Communion" and "Ash Wednesday." Her ignorance of the rites of the Catholic Church was at first treated kindly by her peers ("none of them had ever heard of a church so poor that it had no priest"), but their condolences soon shifted: " 'You're gonna to to hell,' they shouted at me."[1]

That early mysterious distancing from the central cultural focus of the community, combined with a natural curiosity and considerable native intelligence, led to the creation of an astute cultural observer. Her further isolation within her community by attending an exclusive school in "gringo-land" during her impressionable high school years enhanced her sense of herself as an observer. The viewpoint of the self-conscious observer of culture is perhaps the most often and most powerfully expressed in all of poetry. Of course, the empowerment came from Tafolla having lived these crucial years simultaneously within and outside of the culture she loves. Most Chicana (and Chicano) writers have been affected by living in the borderlands between cultures, a state of mind reflected generally by bilingual code-switching, but Tafolla's between-ness is even more pronounced. It has become, in fact, a studied position.[2]

As part of the 1972 Creative Arts of San Antonio Project, this unofficial "observer" became official when she compiled a collection of folktales and folklore from elderly residents of westside San Antonio; the poet was stockpiling images and studying voices that would emerge in her series of poems, "Los Corts."[3] Tafolla's emergence as a major Tejana poet was still a decade away. First came career, education, family.

After completing her M.A. in education (at age 21) at Austin College in Sherman, Texas, Tafolla joined the faculty of Texas Lutheran College in 1973 as director of the Mexican-American Studies Center. In 1976, she coordinated a program producing Multimedia Parent Training Packages for the Southwest Educational Development Laboratory. Soon afterwards, Tafolla became head writer for the pioneering bilingual children's television program, *Sonrisas*, nationally recognized at the time and since as a major step forward in this realm of education. She received her Ph.D in bilingual education from the University of Texas in 1982. Tafolla taught there and in Del Rio, Eagle Pass, and Austin, until she became Associate Professor of Women's Studies at California State University at Fresno. Next, she served as the "cultural diversity programming" Special Assistant to the President at Northern Arizona University at Flagstaff. Late in 1990, Tafolla returned to Texas when her husband, Dr. Ernesto Bernal, accepted the position as Dean of Education at the University of Texas/Pan American in McAllen. When she is not busy writing or giving poetry readings, Tafolla continues to be a sought-after educational consultant.

Like other Tejana poets, she began by publishing her first poem in*Caracol* (1975). The next year, her work was included in the University of Texas/ Center for Mexican-American Studies'*Hembra* anthology and in *Travois: An Anthology of Texas Poets*. Tafolla was one of the three poets (with Cecilio García-Camarillo and Reyes Cárdenas) included in*Get Your Tortillas Together* (1976).[4] Her poems have appeared regularly in numerous anthologies and literary magazines since, but her only full-length volume of poetry to date is *Curandera* (1983), which some Chicana scholars regard as something of a core document. The most notable pieces in the book are the five "Los Corts" poems, each written in a different voice, some of which derived, as mentioned, from Tafolla's 1972 research into the folklore of the westside barrios. Her collection, "La Isabela de Guadalupe y otras chucas," was published in*Five Poets of Aztlán* in 1985,[5] which contains several revised poems from*Curandera*. The poem sequence "Sonnets to Human Beings," published here for the first time, won first place in the 1987 National Chicano Literary Competition (University of California at Irvine) and was accepted for German translation and publication by Wurf Verlag of Osnabrück Universität in 1992.

Besides poetry and television scripts, Tafolla is the author of*To Split a Human: Mitos, Machos y la Mujer Chicana* (1984),[6] a socio-political study of Chicanas, and numerous articles in bilingual education and Hispanic art and literature. *Patchwork Colcha*,[7] a bilingual collection of poems, stories, and songs for children, was published in 1987, and several of Tafolla's children's stories have been included in elementary school readers from the major textbook companies.

As already mentioned, code-switching in Chicana/Chicano poetry is a natural reflection of living on the "borderland between cultures." Like her sense of herself as an observer within, Tafolla's code-switching is both a natural product of her environment and a carefully studied aspect of her craft. In *Curandera* and other early poems, Tafolla's use of code-switching is similar to that of her westside *camarada* Evangelina Vigil, which is to say, she uses a particular westside bilingual dialect rather than simply inserting Spanish words or phrases for effect — not only the use of Spanish itself, but the use of a particular dialect conveys cultural information. In poems of personal statement, mainly in more recent work, and in poems not evoking any geographically specific aspect of Chicano culture, however, her Spanish is often a rich and flawless (and studied) Castilian. As Rolando Hinojosa wrote in his preface to Curandera: *"Tafolla sabe quien es y de donde viene; conoce y aprecia sus raíces méxico-texanas, maneja que no manipula el idioma, y lo encaja donde cabe y debe. Parece cosa fácil pero no lo es."* ("Tafolla knows who she is and where she comes from; she understands and appreciates her Mexican-Texan roots, she controls her dialect without manipulating it, and she uses it when it is fitting and proper. This may seem easy, but it is not.")[8] Santiago Daydi-Tolson identified "at least three language registers, perhaps four, depending on the persona adopted as the speaker of the poem."[9] This is, of course, true of her English as well, something which should give pause to critics who would make too much of any poet's use of two languages. More, even, than being writers, true poets are listeners and observers. Tafolla is certainly a true poet, and she simply has an excellent set of ears and eyes. As she herself has pointed out:

> My favorite style and approach are to write in the voices of people, to let poetry or prose come in their words and thoughts, *and* to let it come in their language and accent, be that good-ol'-boy English or my native language, Tex-Mex. I like my works to understand, to *profundizar*, people — to reveal our strengths and our weaknesses, our struggles and victories and failures and flaws, and, ultimately, our beauty as human beings![10]

Many of Tafolla's most memorable poems in *Curandera* (and reprinted in this collection) recount her middle school experiences, most of which focus on the "struggles and victories" of Tafolla and her peers. In "and when I dream dreams . . ." the young poet witnesses the rapid demise of students who flee the school's institutionalized subservience training where "the lockers of our minds . . . were always jammed stuck" into whatever alleys of hope or oblivion offer themselves — into the military because "war looked easy (compared to here)," into the workplace where a twice-pregnant 15-year-old works 16-hour days, into drugs, into "dropout droppings, prison pains, and cop car's bulleted brains." These things haunt the poet who hangs her "honorary junior school diploma" next to her Ph.D because it means:

I graduated
from you
and when I dream dreams,
— how I wish my dreams
had graduated too.

And, again, we hear the echo of the poet's inner conundrum — the sense of oneness with, and isolation from a reality she has physically escaped, yet emotionally tied herself to by becoming, par excellence, a chronicler of that reality.

Regarding her first encounters with "serious" education, we can hear Tafolla's blood boil in "Quality Literature," a prose poem vignette. The student portrayed in the poem asks his professor to let him write a paper on a Chicano author, only to be told that "Chicano literature simply isn't quality," after which he is directed to read Beckett's *En Attendant Godot*, which "is really superb in its handling of the alienation of the individual in society," etc. A litany of the best Chicano authors follows, all of which are deemed inappropriate until the professor erupts:

[. . .] "But it hasn't even been critiqued in the PMLA! And *until* it's been critiqued in the PMLA, I *can't* say it's quality literature!"
    And the professor walked off into a semi-colon . . . as the face of the student became an epic poem.

This sort of bravado is capable of flights of fancy as well, as when Tafolla imagines herself the fourth of Columbus' ships in "Voyage," one of the poet's most anthologized works. Deceptively simple, this poem bridges that often indefinable gap between poetry for adults and poetry for children. The poem is also critical to the body of Tafolla's work in that it expresses in the clearest sort of metaphor her concept of her role as observer. As the "fourth ship," she delights in the gulls, the sunsets, the "moonbreezes and starvision nights" while the other ships "set their charts" and "point their prows," intent in a businesslike manner on reaching their goal:

I was the fourth ship.
    Playfully in love with the sea,
    Eternally entwined with the sky,
    Forever vowed to my voyage,
    While the others shouted "Land."

Never expressed directly, but lurking at the back of the reader's mind, is the violence that portends once contact is made. That Tafolla can celebrate the brave spirit, whether it is curiosity or adventurism, that pushes humans beyond one horizon after another while remaining conscious herself of the painful results of this particular voyage of "discovery" is evidence of her ability to see both sides of even the most delicate cultural questions. On another level altogether, the observant spirit, the fourth ship, can be understood as revealing Tafolla's concept of herself as a poet — as contrasted to the overly political aims of so many other "movement" poets.

Similarly, she reimagines the character of Marina, *la Malinche*, in her "La Isabela de Guadalupe" collection, (and reprinted in this volume) differently from most other Chicana or Chicano writers. "Yo soy la Malinche," she declares, and she is as feisty as was the poet's fourth ship — and daringly prophetic as well. "Not as others have defined her," wrote Elizabeth Ordonez, "but as she defines herself: daring, decisive, and visionary. In the final lines of the poem, the reborn Malinche issues a cry from gut level to replace the violated, passively silent flesh of the old Malinche with the prophetic greatness of the new:"[11]

But Chingada I was not.
  Not tricked, not screwed, not traitor.
For I was not traitor to myself —
    I saw a dream
      and I reached it.
      Another world...

          La raza.

          la raaaaaaa-zaaaaa...

"I saw a dream / and I reached it" — this is what fires Tafolla's writing, as it has her dedication to her professional life of promoting multicultural understanding. The observer caught between realities, cultures, -isms, must always pay a price — like the accusation of being *la chingada cultural* or *la chingada political* — but the rewards of success are substantial and, in the long run, obvious to all the players.

NOTES

1. Carmen Tafolla, "I was a Barrio Protestant: The True Confessions of Carmen Tafolla," unpublished (1989). The point of this essay is not merely to describe Tafolla's childhood; it takes a wickedly ironic look at the "true Chicano" syndrome of the latter days of the movimiento.

2. See Tafolla's *To Split a Human: Mitos, Machos y la Mujer Chicana* (San Antonio: Mexican-American Cultural Center, 1984), where she discusses at length the struggle "on a borderland between two forces," in this case sexism and racism, which she breaks down further into racism, sexism, racist anti-sexism, and sexist anti-racism.

3. "Los Corts" appear in Tafolla's *Curandera* (San Antonio: M&A Editions, 1983).

4. Carmen Tafolla, Cecilio García-Camarillo, and Reyes Cárdenas, *Get Your Tortillas Together* (San Antonio: Rifan Press, 1976).

5. Carmen Tafolla, "La Isabela de Guadalupe y otras chucas" in *Five Poets of Aztlán*, Santiago Daydí-Tolson, ed. (Binghamton: Bilingual Press, 1985),

pp. 165-210.

6. See note 2.

7. Carmen Tafolla, *Patchwork Colcha* (Flagstaff: Creative Educational Enterprises, 1987).

8. Op. cit., p. 9.

9. Op. cit., p. 49.

10. Carmen Tafolla in *Common Bonds*, edited by Suzanne Comer (Dallas: SMU Press, 1990), pp. 337-338.

11. Elizabeth J. Ordonez, "The Concept of Cultural Identity in Chicana Poetry," in *Third Woman II*, 1 (Bloomington: 1984), p. 76.

Carmen Tafolla

Yolanda Broyles González
University of California, Santa Barbara

BOOKS: *Get Your Tortillas Together*, by Tafolla, Reyes Cárdenas, and Cecilio García-Camarillo (San Antonio: Caracol, 1976); *Curandera* (San Antonio: M&A, 1983); *To Split a Human: Mitos, Machos y la Mujer Chicana* (San Antonio: Mexican American Cultural Center, 1985).

OTHER: "La Isabela de Guadalupe y otras chucas," in *Five Poets of Aztlán*, edited by Santiago Daydí-Tolson (Binghamton: Bilingual/Editorial Bilingüe, 1985).

Carmen Tafolla is among the foremost Texas poets to come out of the post-1960s Chicano experience. With most writers of the Chicano Movement, she shares a deep consciousness of social injustice, an identification with life in the barrio, and a thorough knowledge of her cultural heritage. Her poetry first came to public attention at a Floricanto festival (Austin, 1975) and in the magazine *Caracol*.

Mary Carmen Tafolla was born and raised in the west side barrio of San Antonio, Texas. In unpublished autobiographical notes she said that on her mother's side she comes from "a long line of metalworkers, maids, nursemaids . . . , [and] servantpeople"; on her father's side there were "preachers, teachers, vaqueros (ranch-hands), and storytellers." It is, in part, because of her awareness of her ancestors that Tafolla has developed her clear sense of Chicano identity and of history. Her poetry is rooted in a collective identity: "The people of my family's past, the myths and heroes and characters they painted with their words and with their eyes are alive in me today, as are the people of my past and present. . . . They are all still alive in my mind, as they are in the lives of those today who reflect them and their actions. It's not that my poetry is nostalgic — it's prophetic. History is not there for history's sake; it is there to help describe and decipher the present."

Tafolla spent the first eight years of her education in exclusively Chicano schools. She was awarded a scholarship to an academically oriented private high school. She has written poetry since she was a teenager. Tafolla earned a B.A. in Spanish and French (1972) and an M.A. in education (1973) from Austin College, Sherman, Texas. In 1981, she completed the Ph.D program in bilingual education at the University of Texas, Austin. She has taught at both the high school and university levels. From 1973 to 1976, and in 1978 and 1979, she was director of the Mexican American Studies Center at Texas Lutheran College in Seguin, Texas. In 1984, she accepted an appointment as associate professor of women's studies at California State University, Fresno.

Her husband, Ernesto Bernal, is also an educator and the inspiration for several of her love poems. A woman of versatility and wide-ranging interests, Tafolla has worked as a folklorist, an educational researcher, and a writer for both television and the movies. Her poetry has been included in numerous anthologies.

Among Tafolla's most characteristic and powerful poems are those in which she brings barrio personalities to life using their own voices. She does not purport to speak for Chicanos in an obtrusive or omniscient tone of advocacy or political radicalism. Instead, in her poetry the disenfranchised speak for themselves in their own language. Typical figures are a young school dropout, an old woman, a young pachuca (female hoodlum), a mother, and a little boy who has found a dime. Tafolla shows a rare sensitivity toward the registers of barrio speech of persons from various age groups and walks of life.

In addition to poems written entirely in the voices of barrio heroines and heroes, Tafolla has written poems in which third-person comments are interwoven with the barrio voices. A unifying thematic feature of this group of poems is the spirit of self-determination in the face of adversity, whether that adversity be the result of racism in the schools, inferior educational programs, economic deprivation, or poor housing. The poems of commentary, among which are "Tía Sofía" (Aunt Sofia), "Esa Casa Ya No Existe" (This House Does Not Now Exist), and "19 años" (19 Years), center on self-preservation, human dignity, and the maintenance of Chicano values and culture.

Tafolla's belief in the validity of the oral tradition of Chicano literature leads her to question the professed validity and authority of print. The prose poem "Historia Sin Título" (Untitled Story), from *Five Poets of Aztlán* (1985), illustrates the disparity: "Y ya entendí / Que ellos ni sabian lo que 'taba pasando, porque they had learned it de los libros que had learned it de los otros libros, y nadie sabía ni pensar." (Now I have understood / that they did not even know what was happening, because they had learned it from the books which had learned it from other books, and nobody even knew how to think.)

Many of the poems by Tafolla first published in *Get Your Tortillas Together* (1976), a volume which also includes verse by Reyes Cárdenas and Cecilio García-Camarillo, appear in *Curandera* (Healer Woman, 1983) and in "La Isabela de Guadalupe y otras chucas," her contribution to *Five Poets of Aztlán*. For this reason, it is difficult to speak of Tafolla's development, but her poetry falls into thematic and linguistic clusters. Closely related in sentiment to her commentary poems — but separated from them by linguistic and imagistic differences — are her many poems of remembrance and recollection which are generally restrained in tone. Human memory, the storehouse for oral culture which is the means of transmission of the collective Mexican, Chicano, and Indian traditions from generation to generation, figures prominently in Tafolla's work as it does among most writers of the Chicano Movement. Many of her poems center around remembrance of ancestors and family elders. Notable examples are "Como un Pajarito" (Like a Small Bird), "Curandera," "Memories," "Tía Sofía," and "Ancient House." In "Ancient House," the spirit of an old dying woman in a house "engraved with the secrets and scars of 5 generations" is absorbed into the young speaker:

In that tall-ceilinged ancient eight-walled house
   owned by cold drafts and volcanic spaces
I breathe in through her onionskin lungs
     and know,
with her eyes too old to need vision to see
      that she
        is
        me.

Similarly, in "Curandera," the speaker physically merges with the world of the wise healer:

Curandera,
   te siento arrastrando tus chanclas por los arcos-portales
     de mis venas,
   bajando los botes de tu sabiduría del gabinete
     de mi cabeza

(Healer woman
   I feel you dragging your worn shoes through the arched
     portals of my veins,
   taking down the bottles of your wisdom from the cabinet
     of my mind.)

Other of Tafolla's poems of recollection define the Chicano cultural heritage through nature imagery. Terms such as *venado* (deer), *coyote, cactus, mesquite beans*, and *conejos* (rabbits) connote the Native American ancestry of the Chicanos, often present only at the subconscious level, as in the poem "Aquí" (Here):

He shops the windows, happy,
Where the stalking once was good
and his kitchen floor is built on bones
of venison once gently roasted.

[. . .]

He feels the warmth
and doesn't know his soul is filled
with the spirit of coyotes past.

Her poem "Dead Lipán Apaches" suggests that the Apaches are merely presumed dead. The Indian heritage is in the Chicano present, even when, as in the poem "Warning," it is denied by "a brown ghost / who keeps starving white / and dying brown." In "Memories," the poem's persona speaks of "lavando la herencia" (washing the heritage) in the life-giving artery of the Medina River. Similarly, in "Caminitos" (Pathways), the "pathways of my thoughts" meander with the Medina River and end up:

[. . .] in the monte, chaparral

[. . .]

remembering venado,
remembering conejos,
remembering
where
we came from.

Tafolla's intense sense of rootedness in her heritage, however, is in no way indicative of a static view of culture. In the poem "444 Years After," cultural practices are shown as dynamic, in constant transformation and adaptation. Our Lady of Guadalupe — the most revered Chicano spiritual symbol — is worshiped in modern fashion:

If I gathered roses for you [. . .]

[. . .]

would my jeans jacket sprout
an embroidered vision
of the same old Lupe
with stars in her cloak
but standing on a pick-up
truck with melons?

Both historical and personal memory for Tafolla are strongly matrilineal, and a constant in her poetry is the poor woman who succeeds in spite of poverty. Her female figures are not described in intellectual images; they speak in their own words or are described in a colloquial language that relies heavily on images from everyday life and various rhythmic effects such as incantational repetition. Even in the most adverse situations — such as impoverishment or prostitution — Tafolla's women generate an indomitable will to endure and survive. Through her women figures, Tafolla redefines the concept of strength. Strength is not power over others but is self-directed. It is self-empowerment even if only through spiritual rebellion. The nineteen-year-old prostitute in "19 años" illustrates this concept of power: "Por tanto que me chingan de afuera / no me pueden chingar el corazón" (As much as they may violate my body / they cannot violate my heart).

Another powerful person is La Malinche, the Indian woman Malintzín Tenepal (Hernán Cortés' interpreter, adviser, lover), who is traditionally regarded as a traitor. In "La Malinche" Tafolla has her tell her story in the first person, describing her historical role as that of a visionary of "Another world — a world yet to be born."

"La Malinche" and "La Isabela de Guadalupe y el Apache Mío Cid" are among the few Tafolla poems in which male figures appear as foils addressed by the female poetic persona. In "La Isabela," Tafolla explores the historical unity of opposites found in the sexual union of men and women whose backgrounds, over time, necessarily include mixtures of social classes and ethnicities. Most of the views on women that she expresses in her poetry are elaborated in her prose work, *To Split a Human: Mitos, Machos y la Mujer Chicana* (1985), which addresses problems such as stereotyping, institutional sexism, and racism as they affect Chicanos.

Tafolla's move from her native Texas to the state of California in 1983 demanded considerable readjustments and caused some changes in her writing. It inspired her work on her first novel, "The Land of the Locos," and for the first time Tafolla is writing the great bulk of her work in prose. Her recent poetry shows a heightened mastery of a colloquial poetics and a more contemplative style. In 1987, her most recent collection of poems, entitled "Sonnets to Human Beings," won the first prize in the poetry division of the Annual Chicano Literary Contest at the University of California, Irvine.

WORKS CITED

Reyes Cárdenas, "Las Carnalas Poetas," *Caracol* (September 1975): 17.

Cárdenas, "Crisis in Chicana Identity," *Caracol* (May 1977), 14-15.

Santiago Daydí-Tolson, Introduction to *Five Poets of Aztlán*, edited by Daydí-Tolson (Binghamton: Bilingual/Editorial Bilingüe, 1985).

Papers: Tafolla's papers are held in the Nettie Lee Benson Collection, Latin American Collection, University of Texas at Austin.

VII.
Appendix

Listen to the Voices:
A Conversation with Carmen Tafolla*

Dorothy S. Schmidt
University of Texas – Pan American

DS: In the past, you've talked a lot about your roots, about growing up in San Antonio and the influence that had on your writing and your life. Have you ever thought of going back there?

CT: Oh, yes! Sometimes I think that every time I write, I go back there. I identify so closely with San Antonio, with this area of the country. I love it deeply, yet at the same time, I'm really glad that we had a chance to live elsewhere. That's allowed me to touch a little bit of the soul, to become a little bit of the heart of Fresno and San Bernardino, California, and Flagstaff, Arizona. It's important for a writer not just to visit places, but to live side by side with the people there. So, I have really enjoyed living elsewhere in the Southwest, and it's been an important influence on my work.

I feel that when we go back to who we really are, when we touch our own authenticity, when we become accepting of who we are at our naked reality, that's when we are most capable of touching all of the human beings in the world. It sounds contradictory, but when we're most individual, we're most universal. When we go way down deep into who we are, we touch other people who are way down deep inside, too. That's what I find happening all the time in my writing. When I go to my roots, or to my differing from the norm, or to any of those things that make us individuals, then other people say, "Oh, my gosh, that poem really touched me!"

When I first wrote the poem, "Tía Sofía," for instance, one of my essays in progress was "I was a Barrio Protestant, the True Confessions of Carmen Tafolla." For a long while, I didn't write about the fact that I'd been raised a Protestant, because it made me a minority within a minority [laughs]. You can only go through so many logarithmic levels of "minority-ness" before someone's going to say, "This is a really weird person."

So when I wrote "Tía Sofía," I had no idea of sharing it with anybody else, except possibly my cousin, who had been raised in the same weird family. I thought only she would understand what it's about. The first time I read it in public, almost on impulse, it was to a group of writers, poets, in Austin. I thought, "Well, they'll be more sensitive." They really responded to this character, so then I read it for another group, and another, and then I read it to a mainly Anglo audience and a mainly Black audience, and they identified with it, and I thought, "Why? This is really

---

*Interview in McAllen, Texas, 1992.

weird." I thought nobody would identify with this poem except somebody who'd been raised in a Mexican, Protestant family which was very conservative and very, very traditional, a large family with some weird aunt who acted like Tía Sofía. And yet, people identified.

DS: Probably because every family does have an "Aunt Sophie."

CT: I guess it's because she's really different, and underneath it all, each one of us is really different, too. That's one example of going into your own uniqueness and finding out that, through the intensely personal, you reach the universal.

DS: Look what you've done. I asked you about San Antonio, about a place, thinking that you might respond like Rudy Anaya. For him, the landscape assumes almost mythical powers, as it does for other writers. You responded briefly about place, but then you moved very smoothly and rapidly into what appears to be your major interest, and that is people. It seems that when you think of San Antonio, you're thinking not so much of a geographic location or a historical site or any of those things, but you're thinking of the people.

CT: Yes, I think so, because I see place the same way I see language. Language does not usually have a magic of its own, only the magic that we, as people, give it. Words mean what we think they mean, so that a word that is holy in one language is a curse in another language. And yet, words can carry on the spirit that we leave in them. That's the way I see places.

I love, I dearly love, the dirt of San Antonio. When I was about twelve or thirteen years old, and other people talked about collecting stamps or rocks or other things, I just couldn't get excited. Instead, I started collecting dirt samples, because dirt was a tie to the earth, to the place. The big find for me in high school was when a friend . . . from what I considered a very wealthy family at the time, because my family didn't have a camera for a long time — this person not only had a camera, but it was a 35mm which used these little metal film canisters. These canisters were perfect for my dirt samples. I still have them in the closet somewhere, a bunch of old dirt samples, a mini-Earth. But I used to look at them and think, "This is the dirt from the front baseball field of the junior high, or this is the dirt from my grandparent's house." I take the word earthy literally; I feel a magic about dirt; I feel a magic about San Antonio, but it's only magic because of the people. I look at this dirt, and I say, "Gee, my great-grandfather stood here on this dirt and put away his gun at the end of the Civil War, or my great-great-grandmother washed this piece of dirt out of her clothes." So, in my mind it's hard to separate people from places.

I think people leave behind their memories and their love and their dreams in places. I've walked into houses where I feel the presence of people in the house, even though they might have died five years before; that house just maintains something of that person's spirit. You can feel the tension in a room where there's been a argument, even if the people are no longer there, or you can feel the love in a house, even if the people are not in the house when you enter. So, it's hard for me to separate place from what it means to people.

DS: In several of your poems there is that sense of almost a ghost-like quality, as in "Ancient House."

CT: In a way, *all* of my poems carry ghosts — of the people and places and events that have left their spirit in me. The house in "Ancient House" was my grandparents' house, and then it passed to my aunt. The family had moved into this big old Victorian home in the early 1920s. In the 1980s, my elderly aunt was going to sell the house, and to me that sounded almost sacrilegious, or like abandonment.

Illogical as it was, we tried to buy the house. We were living in California; what did we need a house in San Antonio for? We didn't have the money to do it as an investment, and we couldn't live in it long distance, but I wanted to buy that house. We tried, but some technicality with FHA got in the way. Financially, that was a lucky thing; we would have been hanging ourselves to buy it, yet emotionally, spiritually, it was hard to let go of the place that had seen so many generations, babies, deaths, so many things happen. But I feel lucky that I have the rocking chair from that house and the old chamber pot that no one wanted and the kitchen table. Those are the pieces of the place that I've taken with me. Does that sound materialistic? I'm not a materialistic person, but I'm a sentimental person.

DS: A person involved in parapsychology once claimed that he could take a phonograph needle and read from the wallpaper or a tabletop and other physical objects in a house the actual sounds and messages and memories imbedded there. That smacks of spiritualism, but I believe that, by keeping some of the furniture, you are actually preserving those happenings.

CT: We carry an awful lot of old rickety things with us. People say, "Why in the world are you moving these things across the country?" But to me, they're of great value for the spirit inside them, and the only thing of greater value is that which does not last — like human beings. Chairs may fall apart, but somehow human beings seem to fall apart sooner — at least sooner than the old, well-made chairs. Human beings are valuable. They're not tangible, not durable; they're not permanent, but spiritually, they are extremely valuable.

DS: Let's talk a little bit more about place. You mentioned having lived in San Antonio, Arizona, California, and now here in the Valley [South Texas Valley], and each of these places that you've lived does have strong Chicano cultures. Would you like to comment on the differences between those places in the Southwest that you've lived in, perhaps in terms of ethnic awareness and ethnic values?

CT: There's a distinct quality to the different subcultures of the Mexican-

American experience. We are varied as a people, and that variety is a wealth, just as the diversity of the ethnic cultures of the U.S. provides an invaluable wealth to this nation. Our diversity as an ethnic group provides a lot of perspective, talent, and dynamic tension. It doesn't take much of a sleuth to find these diverse cultural influences in many Chicano families. For example, in different regions of the Southwest, we have a strong Sephardic Jewish influence in Chicano families; they do not practice Judaism, they don't have the Star of David in their houses, but they are culturally similar in their traditions, values, and bloodlines, and in their approach to family and to God.

We also have an extremely Arabic element coming from the Spanish influence. We have both Native American and European influences in differing proportions in different regions. A lot of cultural tragedies happened in confrontations of Native American and Anglo cultures. Yet Mexican-Americans, with a Native American influence, are raised in an Anglo society and somehow are finding a happy medium between the two. So, I consider that dynamic tension healthy, even though, often, historically, it has resulted in tragedy. I think people can bring together elements of the different cultures and create something stronger.

Living in different parts of the Southwest helped me eliminate some of the stereotypes, too. Texas and California, especially, have had their own set of stereotypes about each other: what the Texans say about the California Chicanos and what the Californians say about the Texans. And this is not just recently. My father sang a song that he had learned from the big teenagers next door when he was five years old, which places the teenagers singing this around 1921. *"Las muchachas de California no saben hacer tortillas, se sientan en la mesa, piden pan y mantequilla."* This is a typical stereotype Texans held about Californians. "Oh, those California girls don't know how to make tortillas, they want bread and butter, they don't speak Spanish." It was good for me to live in California and find people who are just as traditional, just as close to their roots, just as authentic to their heritage. And yet, there are differences. There are regional and cultural differences, the geographic influences, the nearness to the border, the influence of different Mexican ethnic and class groups, of Native American cultures.

The most valuable part of having lived elsewhere was the people I met in priceless friendships. Among them, other writers.

I'm convinced that if had I not lived in California, I never would have met Alex Haley, at least not for more than just a handshake after a talk or something like that. Meeting him was a significant instant for me. I was truly moved.

DS: By his work?

CT: By his work and his friendship, by the kind of person he was, the way he acted.

DS: Alex Haley was very appreciative of your work.

CT: He was. And that shocked me.

DS: Shocked you? Why?

CT: I think that I had spent a long while apologizing for my work, for the differentness of my work. Because it was different from the norm; it was theatrical, it was oral in nature.

DS: But wasn't the first poetry in every language that way?

CT: Yes. But that isn't the style of the time, the "correct" fad for poetry. I met him when he was doing a talk; he was a roving editor for *Reader's Digest* at the time, so I gave him an envelope with my work in it. It was somebody else's idea. They said, "You're going to go to the Haley banquet? Aren't you going to take him some of your work?" And I said, "I can't do that. I mean, poor man, he's coming here to do a talk, and then me burdening him with more work?" And they said, "Well, he's a roving editor. Isn't that what a roving editor is supposed to do?" "Well, yeah. It says it right there on the poster that he's a roving editor."

So I gave him a copy of a prose manuscript that I thought would be appropriate for *Reader's Digest*. Then, as a last minute afterthought, I slipped in a copy of my poetry book, *Curandera*. "Because," I thought, "I'm asking him to do something, I should give him something in return. I don't even know if he likes poetry, but it's a gift. It's something in return for what I'm asking him to do." And so I slipped it in the envelope.

Turns out that was the first thing he read, and he was shocked, too, because he said he received large numbers of really lousy manuscripts. Everybody who saw him wanted to give him a copy of their "Roots." "I looked in to my family history, Mr. Haley, and you gotta read this!"

He called me, and asked to meet me, said he was going to be coming back to Fresno in a couple of weeks and wanted to have supper with me. Well, we ended up inviting him over to the house for enchiladas. I was worried about it being too spicy and whether he might have dietary restrictions, but he said, "Girl, I'm from Henning, Tennessee. I eat what I can get!" And I thought, "Oh, yeah, sure." But, he came over. He loved the enchiladas, and we had a good evening talking.

I knew that people who heard me read poetry liked my poetry. I wasn't so certain that people who "read" it silently would like it. Alex Haley never heard me read. He only read my poems. Then he came over to my house to tell me that he had met a writer — "a world class writer" — me. I was still feeling a little apologetic: "Well, it's only Chicano, Tex-Mex, theatrical, orally-based; I'm a good reader, but maybe I'm not that good a poet," because I was not getting a lot of acceptances from the national journals that wanted poetry that was more visual and more intricate. And my writing was folkloric. But Haley told me, "You remind me of a poet I just met. I just came back from a conference in Paris and there was a poet from Africa. And your writing reminds me of his. This poetry, you're at a world class, a world level."

I didn't know at that time what I now more than suspect. About two years later, I was reading an article by Léopold Sédar Sengkhor, the president of Senegal, and also a poet. I think he was the *Africaniste* poet to whom Alex Haley had been referring. Léopold talked about being criticized by the European writers because his French poetry was not visual enough; it was all oral. It was too tied to the ear and the sound, and it was not visually intricate. It was repetitive, almost monotonous, they said. And he said something like this, "Poetry must be voice and song and story" (ironically, almost the same words I had written in the poem "Hot Line" three years before), and he said that the earliest poetry was built for the ear and not for the eye. "Poetry is audio and not very visual," and then it clicked. This is who Alex Haley must have been talking about. And it was at that point, a significant point in my life, that I said, "Wait a minute. Why am I apologizing for my poetry being good audio poetry instead of being 'silently readable' poetry?"

It was a crucial point. I was writing somewhat like an adolescent who says, "I have a right to do this," but underneath it all, they don't know that they have a right to do it. I was writing, saying, "Well,*I* like it. This is what I want to write, and some people like this," but a part of me had wondered: if I were a *better* writer, would my poems have more visual and intricate qualities? In this interview with Léopold by Ann Neelor in the *American Poetry Review*, he talked straight out and said, "I don't apologize for this." When I read this excellent article, it sounded so much like a voice inside of me. Here was a man halfway across the world saying the same thing, going through the same struggle. That was the point at which I said, "This is what my poetry is, this is the voice, these were the voices of the people. If you like what I write, don't honor me, don't compliment me, compliment those people whose voices I captured. They are the ones who are living out the poems in their lives, like the last line in the poem "Quality Literature," where the student's face becomes an 'epic poem.' Those are the people that the poetry comes from; the people are the essence of what I write."

DS: And that is what makes your work so authentic. Let me share an observation with you. A Mexican-American woman in my creative writing class wrote a poem because she was appalled that her students had no appreciation for Hispanic music. She wrote eloquently about the elements of sound and tradition in the music, and admonished the youngsters to simply open their ears and listen. When she finished her reading of the poem, I looked at her and said, "Your poem is well-crafted, rather formal, academic English, but you're talking about ethnicity; why didn't you use at least some Spanish words to help make your point?" She looked at me in a puzzled way and said, "What are you talking about?" I said, "You need to read more Carmen Tafolla."

CT: That's not atypical because, as Mexican-Americans, our academic life is in English. Our home life or personal life has been traditionally in Spanish, so it is not surprising that her poems are more academic when they are written in the English language. We misunderstand language a lot in the U.S. because we are such a publicly-monolingual nation. There's a lot of misperception, misunderstanding about how languages work at the public level. Too many people believe the bottle theory: if you fill up the bottle with too much Spanish, you won't have enough room for English, or if you're going to learn English, you've got to quit speaking Spanish. Not true.

The most important misperception that I run across is that languages are equivalent in translation, but the French student who takes the sentence, "I am going to go my brother's," and looks up each word in a dictionary, will end up with a totally incomprehensible construction. There is no such thing as straight translation. There are few equivalent translations. Languages say different things. Like the old joke, you can't get there from here; you can't say *that* in *this* language; you have to say something similar, but it's not the same thing. So that's why it was so important for Chicanos in the early Chicano literature to use what was a hybrid language because our language could not be expressed perfectly in straight Spanish or in straight English, it had to be in the language that was reflective of our reality — a mixed borderlands language with experiences that came from both of those two worlds.

DS: Do you ever despair that it's going to get better?

CT: I think things *have* gotten somewhat better, but just because we've been at it for so long. The old saying in Spanish, "*Más sabe el diablo por viejo, que por diablo*" (the devil knows more because he's old, than because he's the devil). You learn some things with age. All of us who were young Chicano writers in our twenties are now in our forties, fifties, sixties, but we keep at it, and something is happening, basically because we've been so stubborn about it. Things get better, but people still keep making the same old mistakes over again; we still hear the same arguments we heard thirty years ago. We see the same attempts to move upward and advance by trying to imitate an Anglo ideal. We still see some of our people thinking it's more chic to have things and be things that are typically Anglo-American than things that are typically Mexican-American. I'm not saying we have to avoid other cultures, but neither should we put our culture so far below the others that we don't see the wealth right in it.

DS: It seems to me that such awareness and acceptance of one's culture still involves swimming upstream, tightrope walking. I overheard a scrap of conversation on campus the other day. A student was exclaiming, "Pan dulce! I haven't eaten pan dulce for breakfast since I was three years old! Just because I'm Mexican doesn't mean I eat pan dulce for breakfast!" Evidently some professor had made an unfortunate generalization, and the young man was offended by the assumption.

CT: Yes, some of it's fighting stereotypes, but some of it's still looking to impress others (or ourselves) with so-called "prestige" cultures and actions. There's a lot of acculturation happening; fortunately there's a lot of continued immigration from Mexico, so we have a continuous replenishing of the Spanish language and Mexican culture.

DS: That is a good thing because many languages seem to be losing out to English, even overseas. A recent newspaper article announced that public schools in the Netherlands are going to be taught in English; their university classes already are. So it looks as if, someday, there won't even be a choice of Low Dutch or High Dutch; instead there may be *no* Dutch language. How do you feel about such losses?

CT: It's sad, and yet losses are a part of life. Historically, you can't deny that some things have been lost. Who speaks Karankawa anymore? Who speaks Lipán Apache anymore? Those are the native languages of this area of Texas, and they're gone. It wasn't done in war; it was done in friendly persuasion, and that's what I fear. In the days when I grew up in school, when Spanish was against the state school laws, we had a reason to defend our culture: "That mean teacher isn't going to take my Spanish away from me." But in these days, when someone can smile and say, "That's very nice, but now can you say it in English?" many more kids lose their Spanish. It's no longer a part of their immediate culture; it's part of their tradition or history, but not of their culture for a large number of Mexican-Americans. That's valid, and it has to be recognized as well. Their world is different. Nahuatl is not part of my immediate culture. It's included in my Spanish; it's there in ghost essences and in baby talk, words that are an active part of Mexican Spanish, but Nahuatl itself is not in my immediate culture, even though Nahuatl has survived very well compared to the Native Texan-Indian languages.

DS: So, basically you're saying that even though some of the trappings of culture endure, language can be lost in the very heart of culture.

CT: I think so, or the heart changes; it's a different language. Maybe I'm an optimist, but I don't think any language disappears completely. It would take a tremendously traumatic situation to make it disappear completely. Something is left of it. It's harder to trace, it's harder to see and claim as your own. It's a subtle influence, like going up to Minnesota and listening to the young people of German or Swedish ancestry who say, "Are you going to come with?" and I say, "Come with? You mean, come with me?" They don't realize; they think they're speaking English, but they're really using the grammar of Germanic languages; their English is influenced by it. That influence lasts a long while.

I think languages have to change; I'm not opposed to change in languages or in cultures. I'm not a traditionalist in the sense that we must maintain the values of our grandparents; our grandparents lived in a different world, but I think they have something to add to our world. The culture that doesn't change, dies; the language that doesn't grow, dies. This is why I laugh at the people who are so negative about Tex-Mex, who say, "How can we allow this English to intrude on our Spanish, or this Spanish to intrude on our English?" But intrusion is infusion, and infusion creates growth. The Spanish is enriched by the English elements, and the English is enriched by the Spanish elements. Perhaps in the same way English was born of its own "Tex-Mex" mixture: Latin, Celtic, German, Saxon, a new language could be born in the Americas, an American language that is a mixture of Spanish, English, perhaps French, Vietnamese. There are many processes that a language goes through, and language is critical to writers. Writers have to capture the words that mean something to the people.

DS: I was going to ask if you have a writing routine, but I know that baby Israel, whom you are holding in your arms, greatly affects your time right now. But in general, do you have a particular way in which you've kept yourself going as a writer during those times that menial chores, social functions, professional obligations, and other such distractions rise up and demand your time and attention?

CT: Sometimes they were the stolen moments in the middle of the night. A lot of writers have talked about it, getting up at 5:00 in the morning or staying up when everyone else is asleep. For me, sometimes it requires going away, going to a library or someplace where I have the time to develop something. I hate to be interrupted when I write, especially prose.

The novel I am working on now requires an ongoing involvement. I have to remember what year I'm in, what came before and after. When I go into it, it's kind of like when I do the dramatic performances. I go into the characters. I don't remember what words come on which line next, I just remember who that person is. When I write in the novel, I sometimes don't know what's going to happen next, and I have to go back and ask the character. I have to know the characters; I have to let them live inside of me for awhile, so I really hate interruptions. They're almost like premature deaths for the characters or comments, interruptions of their existence.

For me, the best way is to arrange something that will allow me a three-hour block, anything that will allow me a three-hour block is the best for prose writing; but, it doesn't always work that way. At times, when I am driving someplace, I am composing. I probably have broken many traffic laws because you're not supposed to write a novel and drive at the same time, that's a basic law of traffic.

DS: Do you sometimes take a tape recorder with you?

CT: I should, I just bought one; that's my latest effort.

DS: I tried that once when I was working on an article. I turned the tape recorder on, rolling along the highway dictating. My eyes were open, but I was not seeing, and I almost ran over a line of barriers that were placed in the road. Since then, I have not tried recording while driving because I get too involved.

CT: I've written while driving, waiting in a doctor's office or grocery line, attending a conference, or even speaking on the phone. I take what I can get in terms of writing time. Now, I have done one thing that you're aware of: I used to work at the University for several years, did speaking engagements, and did writing, and you will not be surprised which one of the three got neglected: It was the writing. So I made a law for myself. I made it twice in my life; I broke it once. I made it when I left California, and I made it again when I left Arizona. The law was "Thou shalt not take an eight-to-five job."

I've been fortunate that I can support my writing "habit" by doing lectures and performances. I can give all of my attention to that one talk, to that one performance, and when it's over, it's over. Often, I find I am more creative coming back in an airplane or in a car once the performance is over. I've done my work there, and I leave it behind. But every time I take a regular job at a university, I take my work home with me; even if I don't take it physically, I'm working on it in my head. So, this is something that I've had to do. There are sacrifices for saying, "No, I will not accept this position;" but professionally, financially, whatever the advantages are to a regular job, forget it. I would rather have time to work on my writing.

So, that's what I've done, if I can get three or four days a week when I can block out a morning, then that's it. But sometimes it's 2:00 in the morning, sometimes it's 10:00 at night, or even waiting in the line at the grocery store, with a notepad. Another trick is that I have a lighted notepad by the side of the bed, so I can write in the middle of the night if I need to and not wake everybody up.

DS: I don't dare try that; if I became engaged in writing in the middle of the night, I know I wouldn't get back to sleep again, and the next day would be a disaster. But your schedule is consistent with that of many women writers. Wasn't it Tillie Olson who said that these same sorts of demands and interruptions have silenced many talented women? I'm glad that you persevere.

CT: And I'm really fortunate that I'm being interviewed by another writer because you ask different questions than the people not as involved in literature do. One of the things that I see being asked all the time in writer's interviews is, "Who are the writers who have most influenced your work?"

DS: I don't ask that question because I don't have an answer myself.

CT: I don't either. Everyone influences my writing, and it's not just other writers, it's people. So much of my writing comes out of people that are not writers; some of them may even be illiterate, yet they influence my work.

DS: Here's a question I'm sure *everyone* asks: What are you working on now?

CT: The novel, *La Gente*. I originally wrote *La Gente* as a script treatment for a TV miniseries. I envisioned it and had it sketched out, and everybody kept asking about the novel. I kept saying, "No, I want to do the miniseries first; I'll do the novel later," because I always knew that the novel would take lots of time. A TV script has its limits. You know when it starts and when it ends, but in a novel you really have to set the background for it, so I wanted to do the series first and the novel last.

DS: And was the television miniseries done?

CT: No. And that was my choice. A friend who knows both TV and books used one word, and that one word convinced me. Even Alex Haley had given a copy of the treatment to an editor at Doubleday. And I said, "She's going to look at this and not be interested at all because it's not written as a novel, it's a script treatment." But this friend of mine said the word, "Control." And I said, "Oh yes!" because I remembered what it was like writing for TV.

When a poem is written one way, and the word is there, the comma is there, no one edits a poem. When you write for TV, it's not just edited, it's changed upside down and backwards. Then they put your name to it as if you've written the script. And I'd say, "But, I didn't write that, the way I wrote it was a lot better." So when I remembered that, I said, "Yes, the novel has to come first."

If I wrote the miniseries (it's called La Gente, the people), intending to give a lot of positive messages and portray the variety of our culture, I would write it one way, but then the producer and the director would make all these changes. If I write something that's intended in a positive way, with authentic, rich characters, by the time it hits Hollywood, it could turn out to be a bunch of stereotypes portrayed flatly: This is not what I want.

So even though writing a novel doesn't guarantee anything, there is some conscience that producers have to stick to when they know there is a novel out there. So I'm writing the novel first. And it has grown, it has become an epic, it is much bigger. The miniseries was going to cover a hundred years; already the novel has gone back into the early pre-Columbian period and is coming forward.

DS: Do you suppose eventually it might be a trilogy?

CT: Yes, it's going to have to be. But I'm going to have to draw the line at some point and say this is it; it's over. Cut the umbilical cord and let it go. I feel good about the sections that have been written, and I've gotten positive feedback. I've tried to get the response of not just writers, but of lay people, people who are not involved in Chicano culture. You've got to have a view from the outside as well. I feel good about what I've written; what I've felt bad about is that it's not done.

DS: Do you have a target date for completing the work?

CT: For about the last three years, I've been saying it will be done in nine months, but it keeps growing. I'm going to have to cut it off; it has to be done this year. I can't go past 1992 without it being out[laughs]; that puts it about nine months from now. I would like to have it out this year.

Actually this is not my first novel; I started a novel in California called Land of the Locos. I have sections of that written: I have the ending, beginning, and significant parts in the middle. Land of the Locos was the novel that I was working on when La Gente was conceived first as a miniseries. I had put the miniseries aside until I could make the contact with the appropriate production people, but then I was convinced to do it as a novel, so I'm going to finish *La Gente* first. Then I'll go back to the *Land of the Locos* and finish it up.

DS: Well, that's good. With so much of the work done on it, you could have another novel ready to go within a year of the publication of the first one.

CT: Right, and that book is not a continuation; it would actually be a break from the kind of thinking that goes into *La Gente*. *Land of the Locos* is contemporary, not historical at all, and it's set in an academic environment.

DS: Although they deal with serious topics, such as the struggle of people in the midst of this blended culture, I hope the novels do contain some of the wonderful wit and humor that characterizes your poetry.

CT: I think they do. I think people are funny. I know people say I have a good sense of humor in my writing, but I've never considered myself a humorist. I just consider myself a good scribe; I write down the things that happen around me and a lot of that is so funny.

DS: But it takes a perceptive eye to recognize the cosmic joke that we live in all the time. There are some people who don't have that ability to recognize how ridiculous life is.

CT: I think there's a tremendous amount of irony in the things that happen everyday. *The Land of the Locos* is a serious and somewhat involved tragicomic look at the patterns of oppression, racism, and sexism today, but *La Gente* is just a human comedy; it's human beings in all their ironies, tragedies, victories, the hilarious kinds of things we as human beings do.

My most natural tendency in life is to transcribe what happens around me, and what happens around me is sometimes funny, sometimes sad, but always interesting.

DS: Earlier we talked about writers and the writer's life. Do you have any advice for young writers who don't have a feel for what a battle it's been to be able to write Tex-Mex poetry, who don't have any sense of that long struggle? Are they going to be able to maintain the gains that you and other Mexican-American writers have made?

CT: I don't think I would set myself up as a standard or model that the young writers would have to imitate, for they, too, have mixed languages. I would like them to see their own experiences and possibilities. I simply work from the voice that's inside of me. I would tell young writers that it is important to listen to the voice inside of them. In the process of listening, they open their ears to many voices. They will hear many things that I don't hear, and they will hear languages and experiences that are valid, that others, myself included, might negate, or not consider seriously. Just as for many years Mexican- American writers who wanted to be taken seriously wrote exclusively in English or exclusively in Spanish, trying not to use the vernacular, trying not to capture the experiences they heard at home, young writers today hear things that others may not have captured on paper.

It's important that they listen to the voice inside themselves and be authentic to it, and if they get struck by something in the middle of the night, they should jump up and write it down. And instead of imposing a language on what they are writing, let the language come from the voice inside. I usually don't say I'm going to write this piece in a Tex-Mex, or I'm going to write this piece in a rural Spanish dialect or in an urban mixture of Spanish and English. I recall at certain points saying I'd like to write a poem about this topic, but I don't ever recall having decided the language that it goes in.

DS: Evangelina Vigil noted that most of your love poems are in Spanish, perhaps suggesting that when you dig deep into your own innermost heart and feeling, the voice does speak only Spanish.

CT: Yes, but the best pieces, I think, have come from voices that may not sound like mine but came through me, and I wrote them down. I'll never forget — it was in Flagstaff, Arizona, far from the borderlands. We were up in the mountains, in the snow and the pine forests, different from the traditional stereotype of the Southwest. There wasn't even a tortilleria in Flagstaff, no place you could go buy fresh tortillas. They were in the frozen section in the grocery store, or they were made at home. So we used to invite people over to the house. We'd make a big pot of frijoles a la charra, frijoles borrachos (drunk beans), and we'd make a lot of fajitas, and we'd warm tortillas, and we'd feast.

We'd joke about how we'd smuggle the right tortillas back to Arizona, because California and Arizona have a completely different kind of tortilla than Texas has. So it was a shock once on an airplane to meet somebody who was flying in the opposite direction, flying back home as I was flying away from home, who was smuggling Arizona tortillas back to Texas. I said, "Are you kidding? I smuggle them from Texas back to Arizona!"

When we would have people over, it was part of maintaining the culture, but there was a different feel about a small minority having to really work at maintaining the culture. We weren't the only ones who did this, there were other Mexican-Americans who also made a special effort to bring the kids together, and the families and friends, and create our own cultural source.

But in the middle of one night, there in Arizona, this line came to me: "It all started when Chencho's cow kicked over a pot of beans." I had no idea what a pot of beans had to do with anything at two in the morning, and I wasn't about to get up and write it down. I was tired, I was sleepy, I had been doing some academic work, and I had just laid down. I valued that time to sleep, and I was just beginning to unwind when this line came to me, and I said, "Now, go away," and the line wouldn't go away. I got up and wrote it down, and wrote about a paragraph not knowing where, how, or why, but I wrote it down. I believe strongly in crafting and editing and polishing your work, but I also believe in listening for what García Lorca calls the *duende* — the little elf that has to be present in order for something to have spirit. A dance can be perfect, but if it doesn't have a *duende*, if the *duende* is not there . . .

DS: It's not enlivened by the senses; the spark is not there.

CT: Yes, and Lorca writes an elaborate article on the difference between a *duende* and a muse, and the difference between a *duende* and a demon. It's not the same; a *duende* is not an angel. The *duende* has a spark, and if he's not present, the flamenco dance is technically perfect, but has no fire to it; the poem has beautiful words, beautiful constructs, but they have no soul. I believe in the *duende*. And it got me out of bed and made me write the story, which I think is probably my best short story. And it all started with that pot of beans Chencho's cow kicked over in the middle of the night.

So I would tell writers to listen to experiences, listen to the voices, listen to the languages, try to develop an authentic language. For me, that doesn't mean just one language. Many people have told me I don't have a style, I have several styles. Maybe it's because I grew up in a world that had two cultures and two languages. I got spoiled by the ability to code-switch, to switch between the languages, to switch from the way you talk to the teacher to the way you talk to the other kids, to go from formal English to Tex-Mex, from Texan English to Mexican Spanish.

For whatever reason, I think good writers need to think less of making a name for themselves — "oh, this is the recognizable style of Carmen Taʿolla" — or about what critics are going to say, and listen more to the *duende* inside of themselves. Go deep into what sounds right, even if you can't explain why it sounds right. Maybe later on you'll find out why, when someone writes a beautiful critical essay, and you say, "Ah-ha! This is what it means." There is an intuitive sense to writing, and both writers and readers must tune in to it.

An Interview with Carmen Tafolla*

Teresa Palomo Acosta

Editor's Note: Poet Carmen Tafolla earned a Ph.D in Foreign Language and Bilingual Education from the University of Texas at Austin in 1981. She has held numerous positions as an educator in her field and worked as the Director of the Mexican American Studies Center at Texas Lutheran College. But it is writing that has drawn her creative commitment more than has any other pursuit. *Curandera*, a new collection of poetry, is due out in 1983. In a recent interview with Teresa Palomo Acosta, Tafolla talked about why she writes and why poetry has particularly become so important for her to write.

Q. Do you always know what you're writing about as you're writing? When does it become clear?

A. No, not always. O, let's say, I don't always know the *whole* of it until after I can sit down and examine the work from the perspective of an artist. I very much believe that the art is greater than the artist; that is, the artist is a person sensitive to the world around her, and she or he *taps into* this knowledge, sometimes at an intuitive level — below the level of consciousness, and then tries to express it at a conscious or at least a *public* level. I see the process of writing very much like that of having a child; *you* have the child, but the child can become greater than you, different from you; the child becomes its own person. A piece of writing, an artistic work, has your message and *your* perception of the world in it, but once it goes *out* in the world, it interacts with those who read it, and *may* carry a different message than what you intended. *Hopefully*, it carries the message you intended consciously *plus* all the intuitive wisdom you are tapping into at an unconscious level through your feelings. The good artist is like the Old Testament definition of a prophet — not someone who sees the *future*, but someone who *sees*, who really understands *clearly*, the present. That's *part* of why poetry exists and why I very much want to *devote* myself to being a writer. If we can *see*, really clearly, the world around us, we can help others see it, too, through our writings. In this way, we can help make our world better.

Q. Your forthcoming collection is entitled *Curandera*. How do you define Curandera, and do you see poetry as a healer?

A. Poetry *is* a healer. It doesn't always pamper the wound; it sometimes tears it open to break open the infection and let the pus out. It is hurting sometimes — but it seeks reality. I have seen "false poetry" — stuff that pretends and plays games with words, and worse — with reality. But *that's* not real poetry. *Real* poetry *is* a Curandera — not a sweet and pretty Red

*Reprinted from *Arriba* (October 1983)

Cross Calendar nurse, but an old woman, painfully honest, tough, but concerned with getting you well, emotionally *and* physically, concerned with getting the whole world well. You see, our world is too often a sick one — we see it on the six o'clock news and in the inhumane treatment of people. Maybe this is why our image of the artist is so often of some consumptive character that dies young — because the artist sees the sickness, and it hurts him, *invades* him inside. Today's world is so visibly sick, though, that if we *let* it, even the six o'clock news will *consume* us. And we can't *afford* to be sick and die. As artists and writers, we need to stay healthy, so that we can *curar* this seriously ill world.

Q. Why poetry, or why poetry for you?

A. I think women and minorities and people who find themselves facing a lot of injustice or blindness in the world around them see the *special* need for the arts to help their *survival*. As a Chicana, I feel very strongly that I *need* to make people see, to understand things about us as women, and as a Chicano culture. I think about the public image of this "butterfly-headed artist type" who wanders around "trying to suffer, trying to experience." It's a caricature of the white middle-class kid who has to *seek out* something to feel oppressed or angry or rebellious about. But here *we* are in this world that's full of *real needs, real tragedies, real problems;* all we need to do is to really *see* them, and to help *others* see them; that's why I *write*. But we need to help others *feel* them, too — and that's why I write *poetry*.

Q. I'm very interested in the personal, whispered things and language of gesture as rich mines for writing about. What pulls you toward a poem — remembered things? Something observed? What?

A. Teresa, I really like the way you see poetry as a being, pulling the artist towards it. I agree. It is those whispered things that tell you *what* about the world around you needs commentary. It is usually *people* I write about — the tíos, abuelas, pachucas, the dropouts, chamaquitos. It is those people whose *lives* are poems that create the "portrait poetry" or "voice poetry" I like so much. Often I feel it's not *me* that is the poet. They are! I'm just recording those beautifully human parts of them that I see. Sometimes a poem is hidden in someone's sigh, the worried look of a woman waiting in line, the sweaty, dusty t-shirt of a construction worker in the middle of disrespectful traffic, the cataract in the eye of a viejita. The poems are all around us — in our deepest memories especially, for *that's* what touches our hearts with real significance. *Every person who ever had feelings is a poet; some of us just see it* and write it down as it interacts with our own heart's eye.

Q. Do you write poems in order to understand something you otherwise cannot understand, or to ask questions no one else can ask for you?

A. Both. And more. A poem is like a picture. There's something in *front* that's focused on, and then there's the setting — the table in the background, the pictures on the wall. I want others to be able to *see* what I see. When I first started writing poetry, it was very private; I showed my poems to no one; I wrote them just for me — just to let my feelings out and to be able to pick them up later like photographs, and see something better. I write because I want to understand. Now that I am published, I also write because I want others to ask questions and to see the insides of other people's lives, the insides of their closets, their coffee mugs, their frustrations, their smiles. I think art (and for me, especially poetry) brings us closer together and closer to the meaning of our lives.

Carmen Tafolla's Barrio Voices, the Hispanic Drop-Out Rate, and America 2000: What do They Have in Common?

Guadalupe Ochoa Thompson
Texas A&I University

Carmen Tafolla's video *With Our Very Own Names* gives us a view of the environment of Hispanics, especially in our public school system. Tere, the first grader, expresses her love for learning, but by the time her first day in school ends, she is disappointed and develops a "no importa" (it doesn't matter) attitude that follows her through junior high and makes her a potential drop-out. Tere also encounters the "no Spanish rule" in the playground when she yells "¡Córrele Juanito, córrele!" and the coach admonishes her with "Speak English, we are in the U.S.A."

In junior high, we meet "La Dot" (la pachuquita), who has learned to defend herself and is ready to fight anyone. In this episode, we learn that the school is not worried about their fighting and getting hurt, but about the damages that can occur to the gym floor.

> . . . Ey — la Mary Pester le taba escribiendo dirty notes a La Silvia y ella también patrás — y taban diciendo malas cosas de Teodora. Me dijo Rosie. Y que Manda y Rosie y la Teodora s'iban a juntar en P.E. para dárselo a Pester y a Silvia. — You bet, muchacha! Aquí toy — lista! Ajá, y a ver a quién más juntamos, porque La Silvia se junta con todas esas gordonas feótas que tan pero perras pa pelear. Sí, en las showers, pa que no vea la Miss Hansley, porque no le gusta que peleamos en el gym floor. (Tafolla, 21)

At the university, we meet Beto, who wishes to study and write a critique on a Chicano writer. The English professor, who has not read any Chicano authors, does not give him his approval since "Chicano literature is not quality literature since it has not been critiqued in the PMLA Journal."

Education for these students is disappointment, discouragement, de-education, for they are taught to forget their language and culture, and made to feel inferior. One of the major problems is the insistence on fitting the Mexican-American student into the monolingual, monocultural mold of the Anglo-American.

Let's leave Tafolla's barrio voices and look at every day in America, as researched by the Children's Defend Fund, 1990. Every day in America:

2,740	Teenagers get pregnant
1,105	Teenagers have abortions
369	Teenagers miscarry

1,293	Teenagers give birth
700	Babies are born with low birth weight
69	Babies die before one month of life
107	Babies die before their first birthday
27	Children die because of poverty
9	Children die from guns
6	Teenagers commit suicide
1,375	Teenagers drop out of high school
1,849	Children are abused
3,288	Children run away from home
2,987	Children see their parents divorced
135,000	Kids arrive at school with a gun

During the last decade, the Census Bureau reported a 53% growth in the mainland U.S. Hispanic population. Overall, the Hispanic population grew at a rate five times that of the non-Hispanic population. In Texas, for the first time, minority enrollment exceeds fifty percent, and Hispanic students continue to have the highest dropout rate of any group and the lowest high school completion and graduation rate.

As we look at every day in America, we can see that we have major problems in our society, and added to these are the federal deficit, the trade deficit, the recession, and the lost competitive edge.

Hoping to solve our problems, President Bush and the state governors in 1990 initiated America 2000, which formulated six national goals geared to the improvement of education:

- that all children should be ready for school
- that we should achieve a 90% graduation rate
- that we have proficiency in core curricula
- that we become first in the world in math and science
- that we achieve adult literacy and give everyone the ability to compete
- that we have drug-free and violence-free schools

(America 2000)

Probably if asked, most of us would have come up with a somewhat different list of goals — maybe we would have been more precise and realistic. But as a whole, the goals are a reasonably good statement of national aspirations, and the country will be much better off if we reach the goals than if we do not.

Reaching the goals will require significant improvements in a wide range of services for children, including health care, child care, preschool programs, programs for at-risk students, programs for limited English proficiency students. It will also require a fundamental overhaul of the nation's schools in order to change the voices of Tafolla's barrio children to be the voices of an educational system that has effectively incorporated their welfare and abilities to ensure future leaders and contributing citizens for our nation.

WORKS CITED

America 2000, The National Education Goals, 1990.

Children's Defense Fund Report, 1990.

Tafolla, Carmen. *Curandera.* San Antonio: M&A Editions, 1983.

guages. Formerly at University of Oklahoma (Modern Languages Department), she is presently in the Bilingual Education Department at Texas A. & I., Kingsville, Texas.

Translating/Übersetzen *Sonnets to Human Beings* by Carmen Tafolla

Wolfgang Karrer
Osnabrück University,
Germany

"Übersetzen" (Translating) in German still carries the older meaning of "Ferrying over." This is part of what we tried to do here at the University of Osnabrück, when we first read *Sonnets to Human Beings* in manuscript. The fact that the manuscript ciculated in Germany indicates the close ties Chicano and Chicaca studies have established with some German Universities (Bamberg, Bremen, Erlangen, Germersheim, and Osnabrück being the most important ones at the moment).

Osnabrück publishes a series of bilingual editions, called OBEMA, that tries to introduce the German reading public to the works of minority authors and to help generate a greater international awareness of intercultural relations and relatedness. The series includes authors like Rolando Hinojosa, Peter Blue Cloud, Melba Boyd, and Joseph Bruchac. The texts are studied and translated by a group of students who work together with a professor to prepare the printing and help in the distribution of the volume.

Ours was a mixed group. We had a student from the United States in the team who helped us with some of the problems that dictionaries could not solve, one or two were active in human rights work, two had become specialists in African-American literature. One student was pregnant, another was a poet. Two knew very little Spanish. All brought great enthusiasm and dedication to the work which went through various phases of revision. Carmen Tafolla helped us by mail with the final list of problematic words and allusions. In German, for instance, you have to decide whether "you" means second person plural or singular.

This brings me to the heart of the matter. Translating is more than a ferrying over of cultural cargo from one side of the Atlantic to the other, it also tests commonalities and differences. Minority literatures as well as regional writing are under constant and additional pressure to "transcend their narrow concerns," usually with the advice to reflect the universal in the particular. Pressure and advice usually come from majority critics, and they often define universality in terms of the majority. The so-called "eternal and unchangeable principles of human existence" often serve to disguise cultural dominance – the principles are the habits of the heart among the Anglo middle classes – and to eliminate social conflicts from literature. The title *Sonnets to Human Beings* certainly supports an impression that here is a book by a Chicana writer which transcends all cultural nationalism and addresses humanity in its most universal terms.

Front cover for Sonnets to Human Beings/Sonette an Menschen , *Osnabrück, Germany, 1992.*

This impression is put to a severe test by the reading and translating of the poems collected under that title. What emerges after that test is a far more complex and rooted interpretation of the collection.

Except for the magnificent Shakespearean rhetoric of the concluding "How shall I Tell You?" none of the poems approaches the traditional sonnet sequences or even modernist versions of it like Rilke's *Sonnets to Orpheus* (which are really sonnets of the poet to himself).* And the human beings the poems address are very particular and often very ethnic people: a dead hija, a Chicano veteran, Anglo and Chicano teachers, Central and South American women who died under torture, a Mexican woman during the Revolution, neighborhood people like Concha's brother, a Mexican mother who lost her baby to the Baby Black Market, or simply, an older human. Each poem is carefully encoded in Chicano culture and demands serious attention to it. These human beings refuse easy categorization such as race, gender, or class: they are not always victims, they too are rebels against domination. They have a message for us, if we choose to listen carefully. Another group of poems addresses us as readers in an encompassing "We." These poems come closest to the universalizing tendency so often asked for by critics. "We Never Die," "Around Us Lie," "Living on the San Andreas," "Come With Me People," and "They Come From Within Us" intersect with the poems directed to specific people, the first group, and with the more personal poems where the poet speaks to herself and about her bilingual craft, a third group. The "we" thus bridges the "you" and the "I." And it is carefully anchored in both. No facile synthesis, the "we" is often gendered, clearly a woman speaking, or ethnic, a Chicana voice, through symbolic encoding. The words are "spiritchildren" that come from "the fifth womb/ of the fifth soul" of the collective speaker, "They Come From Within Us", and those readers who do not know about the "Quinto Sol/ Soul" in Chicana literature can find out about it, if they care to go beyond a free-floating signifying universal.

This brings me to the second test of universality: translation. As a translation team we brought our own cultural sensibilities to the texts. Sometimes we simply lacked words, we had to disambiguate the text. For example, how do you translate "fifth soul" into German? Fortunately, we had the original text side by side with the translation. But Sonnets to Human Beings also challenged our bilingual format of the series. The original texts were already bilingual, and they made maximum use of their bilinguality. We decided not to translate certain key cultural symbols from the Spanish, especially if they were repeated, except in a glossary: "comal, Diez y Seis, migra, tecalote," etc. We left Chicano phrases intact if they were repeated and contextualized. We translated Spanish dialogue in "Porfiria," but we put the passages in italics to emphasize difference. Behind this practice stood our conviction that if you translated "comal" by the German word "Tiegel," or "migra" by "Einwanderungsbehörde," you erased something important in the culture that the poem was speaking from. Of course, Germany has a migra, and that Germany is dealing with immigrants in the nineties helps to create an understanding of what Carmen Tafolla is saying about liberty in "Statue of." But the cultural differences would be erased – Germany has undocumented immigration because it does not have an immigration law – and the work

---

*Editors note: Four other Tafolla sonnets (Pedacito, Beyond Our Own, The Magic, and Chispa) now included in this larger collection, were not part of the earlier manuscript translated and published in Germany.

toward understanding what constitutes the "Other" would be aborted.

This work, however, proved to be essential to our understanding of the texts and our intercultural relatedness to them. And the most important part of this work was talking about the texts and our translations. The gendering of the texts – its secret center around giving birth – became clear to us through the pregnant student. I was able to contribute contexts to some of the untranslated Chicano words. The U.S. student told us what the old TV Program "Leave It to Beaver" was all about. Somebody brought us Amnesty International reports about torture in Hispanic America and Human Rights violations in Guatemala. Another student pointed out how "October 21st" was coded in Black American. We discussed together the context of Pueblo sand paintings, the meaning of feathers and turquoise in Native American cultures, the Chicano mythologies, and we talked about Chernobyl and the Persian Gulf. While at work, it became clear to us that the poems spoke to us not simply by appealing to certain universal experiences like love, death, and suffering, but by making us aware that we are connected in a common world that binds us together through human rights, wars and terms of trade, through ecology or mass media. They make us aware that at no moment we are outside this world the poems describe. And if they touch our emotions across the Atlantic, they do so in a very specific and political context of the nineteen eighties and nineties.

This became even clearer after we finished the book, and presented it in a public reading to other students of English and American here at Osnabrück. Each translator presented his or her three favorite poems from the collections, both in American and German, and each talked about what the poems meant to them. Many of the poems had struck deep personal or political chords, and the students tried to transmit these feelings to their audience. They had listened to tapes where Carmen Tafolla had given voice to her speakers in the poems.

When Carmen Tafolla came to Osnabrück in 1993 to read personally from her work and to talk about "Recognizing The Silent Monster: Racism in the 90's," she did not only have an attentive audience which felt that Germany's problems were dealt with here. She had also reached human beings with questions, and her poems had paved the way for this intercultural dialogue which stresses the human commonality, denying neither the cultural differences which constitute our richness nor the forces that menace our humanity. For the *Sonnets to Human Beings* are part of an ongoing larger project in which many writers and readers are engaged. And this dialogue is important for all of us, because words are tools. In Carmen Tafolla's own words:

> The time is past when we could afford to waste human talent and a wealth of perspectives. The time is past when we could take the human race so lightly as to denigrate the contributions of any culture or nation of people. The time is now for writing sonnets to the whole

human race, lest we awake one morning to discover that we as a race, a human race, do not exist anymore.

(Recognizing the Silent Monster: Racism in the 90's")

Now's the time.

Empowering Students Through Creative Writing[*]

Carmen Tafolla

When I was a young child growing up in a Mexican-American barrio, I used to dream of becoming a writer. But, somehow, I had received the message that all writers came from New York and that most novels took place with a backdrop in Central Park. "Alas," I thought, "if only I had been born in New York, I might have had something to write about." My barrio had no Central Park — it had no park at all, only a tortilleria — an old tortilla shop at the end of the block, where an aged woman shuffled out at a snail's pace to take our order. Not only was she aged, but I was convinced at that time that she was the oldest woman I had ever seen alive. Her face was carved of endless, mysterious wrinkles, her white hair seemed to call the sunlight as if they were centuries-old companions, and her earth-colored hands seemed made not of skin, but of the life-giving corn masa itself, which she daily worked and shaped into tortillas — and all sales were placed to order, according to one's means; someone with only seven cents would order seven tortillas, and no one ever figured in tax — this world's oldest woman would shuffle slowly sideways, in successive halting half-turns, as if to almost face the back of this room that turned their house into a family business. Then, she would shout out in a strong but matter-of-fact voice, "Mama!" and her mother would come out to help her turn the tortillas on the flat, black top of the cast-iron stove.

But I thought I had nothing to write about, and that far, far away from the writers' world of New York, I would never become a writer. Somehow, my school experiences only reinforced that message, presenting literary works only from a culture alien to mine, and teaching that appropriate topics for creative writing were those requiring a different set of experiences than my own.

Yet, creative writing can be one of a teacher's most powerful tools in the validation of students' unique individual and cultural experiences, and in their simultaneous nurturance of self-esteem and of student empowerment. The role of creativity in a person's intellectual and personal development is a vital one. W.B. Yeats knew this when he wrote,

> The friends that have it I do wrong
> When ever I remake a song,
> should know what issue is at stake;
> It is myself that I remake.

And it is our students who are trying to "remake" themselves in a world

[*]Reprinted from *Excellence in Teaching*, Winter 1989-90.

that is increasingly chaotic and increasingly dehumanizing. All students suffer to develop and create their own definitions of self-esteem, but it is perhaps those students who most struggle against societal expectations and stereotypes of a lowered self-esteem who are least likely to be encouraged to express themselves creatively. Students from lower socio-economic backgrounds and from culturally or linguistically different backgrounds are frequently pushed into programs that stress the "basics" and the mechanics of writing, while creative writing is often considered most appropriate to those "gifted" children from "advantaged" backgrounds. Many "minority" children (the actual majority of the school-age population in all large urban centers, and the soon-to-be majority of school children across the nation as a whole) are never exposed to long-term creative writing programs, yet these are the students who most have need of these chances to redefine themselves socially and culturally, and of whom our society has the most need.

With the rapid demographic changes that our society is presently undergoing, with the complex problems of alienation, apathy, violence, and meaninglessness, and with the rapid changes that education must undergo if it is to meet our society's needs, we have need of a great variety of new possibilities. We have need of all segments of our society in order to forge these new paths and to empower all of our peoples.

Noted psychologist Rollo May prioritizes the need in his book, *The Courage to Create*, in which he describes four different kinds of courage and concludes that the most important kind of courage is what he calls "creative courage."

> "... whereas moral courage is the righting of wrongs, creative courage . . . is the discovering of new forms, new symbols, new patterns on which a society can be built . . . . In our day, technology and engineering, diplomacy, business, and certainly teaching . . . are in the midst of radical change and require courageous persons to appreciate and direct this change . . . . Thus the artists . . .are a 'dew line' . . . they give us a 'distant early warning' of what is happening to our culture . . . . The artists thus express the spiritual meaning of their culture."

If this creative courage is so essential to our survival as a society, should not we, as educators, be facilitating and developing it in our students? "But how?" my friend, the fourth-grade teacher asks me, "How can I expose them to creative writing if they don't even know how to use a comma, or how to conjugate the verb *be?*" "All the more reason," I answer him, "to give them a *reason* to want to use a comma, to give them a *meaning* to *transmit* with the verb *be*."

Writing is not about structures or rules or even parts of speech. Structures and rules are just tools that writers use to facilitate the transmission of their message. But writing is really about people — it starts with people and it ends up with people. And if we dig deep inside ourselves, we will find that which only *we* and no one else can say to the world. And if we find that which only we can say to the world — we will find that part of ourselves that is the most human, and thereby closest to every other human being on the face of the earth.

And if writing is really about people — their feelings, their ideas, their struggles, their victories and failings, then there is not one of us as educators that doesn't have something to write about. And there is not one of our students that doesn't have something to write about, something very close to their own self-esteem and their own sense of power. We must first of all *allow* them their voices, and then show them the tools from which to select, at *their* discretion, in order to make their voices heard.

Students are often hesitant. They sometimes cannot believe that we really want to hear what they have to say. They may not have been exposed to a diversity of experience in literature. They may think of poetry as "butterflies and sweet stuff" instead of as feelings — good, bad, and authentic. They may think of novels as Bobbsey Twins fare, taking place in Midwestern nuclear families of a dominant culture, dominant experience, dominant pattern that none of us really fit exactly. So, your first step must be to expose them to the great variety of literature. (Minority and regional writers are often your best sources.) One must give before receiving. Helpful steps include:

1. Encourage *play* with words. Let them make up their own rules, so as to better understand why rules exist. Writers are in a constant experimentation with words; so are young children. Riddles and jokes are studies in the power of words.
2. *Give input* before requesting output. Read to students — the fun, the delightful, the scary, the tragic, anything goes — the more honest, the better. Kids have a need for meaning.
3. Legitimize *authenticity*. Let them know they have something special to contribute that only they can give. Include authenticity of concept/culture and language/dialect. Remember, neither Chaucer nor Steinbeck wrote in the "accepted" dialect.
4. Encourage the use of all five senses — and sometimes a sixth! (Allow new concepts in sensing.)
5. Let them do a step-by-step "portrait" of someone.
6. Keep the cart behind the horse! Creativity comes first; criticism follows, *after* the piece is created. Assure them they will have plenty of time to do their own criticism, editing, and rewriting, once the piece is written down. Tell them to block off the criticism until the creation has been allowed to flow out. Then, equip them with tools for improvement, and let them, the crafters, handle the improvements on their own and to their satisfaction.
7. See language as *expansion*, not elimination. (The mark of an educated person is not that they never use "ain't," but that they know when to use it to its best purpose!)
8. Let students become actively *involved* as contributors and creators of language (e.g., letters to the editor, literary festivals, use of language as

action).

Creative writing has no correct answers against which to measure your students' progress, but the rewards are nonetheless massive. These students, from all of their diversity of experience, culture, language, and style, are our answers. They are the answers to our future. They are, out of their own uniqueness and complexity, the resolution to our very complex problems.

And if you are tempted to think, even for a second, that they are too young, too different, too deprived to have anything to write about, let me tell you the story of another young child from a deprived background. Years after dreaming of becoming a writer, she did indeed reach her goal. After publishing four books of poetry, seven screenplays, three children's books, two textbooks, one book of nonfiction, and numerous articles and short stories, she realized that the piece that had been published the most, in the broadest range of publications, and in the most prestigious anthologies, was a poem about an aged Mexican-American woman whose face was carved of endless, mysterious wrinkles, whose white hair called the sunlight, whose earth-colored hands seemed to be made of corn masa, who seemed to be the oldest woman alive, and who would shuffle slowly around to yell to the back of the shop, "Mama!" . . and of her mother, who sold tortillas for a penny each. No tax.

A Selected Bibliography
of Works by Carmen Tafolla

The following writings by Carmen Tafolla are divided into seven categories: Books of Poetry; Non-Fiction Books; Short Stories; Anthologies/Journals/Textbooks/Magazines in which Tafolla's poems have been published; Children's Works; Chapters and Academic Articles; and Screenplays/Other Scripts/Song Lyrics. In addition, it should be noted that the original manuscripts and early writings by Tafolla have been archived in the Mexican-American Archives of the Benson Latin American Collection at the University of Texas at Austin.

I. BOOKS OF POETRY

Sonnets to Human Beings and Other Selected Works by Carmen Tafolla: A Lalo Critical Edition, Santa Monica, CA: Lalo Press, 1992.

Sonnets to Human Being / Sonetta an Menschen, (original and German translation), Osnabrück, Germany: Wurf Verlag Press, 1992

"La Isabela de Guadalupe y otras chucas," in *Five Poets of Aztlán*, Santiago Daydí-Tolson, ed., Binghamton, NY: Bilingual Press/Editorial Bilingüe, 1985.

Curandera, 1st ed.: San Antonio, TX: M & A Editions, 1983; 2nd ed.: La Jolla, CA: Lalo Press, 1987

Get Your Tortillas Together, (co-authored with R. Cárdenas and C. García-Camarillo), San Antonio, TX: Rifan Press, 1976.

II. NON FICTION BOOKS

Recognizing the Silent Monster: Racism in the 90's (Monograph), Edinburg, TX: UTPA American Humanics, 1991.

To Split a Human: Mitos, Machos y la Mujer Chicana, San Antonio, TX: Mexican American Cultural Center, 1983.

III. SHORT STORIES

"Chencho's Cow," *Saguaro*, Tucson, AZ: University of Arizona Press, 1987.

"Federico y Elfiria," *Mosaic*, Riverside, CA: University of California at Riverside, 1987. *Third Woman*, Vol. IV, Berkeley, CA: Third Woman Press, 1989. *Common Bonds: Texas Women Writers*, Dallas and College Station, TX: SMU Press, 1990.

"You Don't Know Marta," *Southern Exposure*, January/February 1986. Also in edited version: "Ladies of the Club," *Third Coast Magazine*, April 1985.

IV. ANTHOLOGIES/JOURNALS/TEXTBOOKS/MAGAZINES

Multicultural Voices, Glen View, IL: ScottForesman, 1995.

**GET YOUR TORTILLAS
TOGETHER**

Cecilio García-Camarillo
Carmen Tafolla
Reyes Cárdenas

Curandera

BY
CARMEN TAFOLLA
Introduction by Rolando Hinojosa

Front cover for first book of poetry, Get Your Tortillas Together, published in 1976.

Front cover for first edition of Curandera, published in 1985.

Paper Dance: 55 Latino Poets, New York: Persea Books, 1995.

In Other Words: Literature by Latinas of the U.S., Houston: Arte Publico, 1994.

Texas in Poetry: A 150-Year Anthology, Denton: Center for Texas Studies, 1994.

Infinite Divisions: An Anthology of Chicana Literature, Tuscon and London: U. of Arizona Press, 1993.

New Growth 2, San Antonio: Corona Publishing Co., 1993.

After Aztlan: Latino Poets of the Nineties, Boston: David R. Godine, 1992.

Puerto del Sol, Vol. 27, No. 1, Spring 1992, Las Cruces, NM.

Riversedge, Vol. V, No. 1, Fall 1990, Edinburg, TX.

Saguaro, Vol. 6, 1980, Tucson, AZ: University of Arizona Press.

An Ear to the Ground: An Anthology of Contemporary American Poetry, Athens, GA and London, England: University of Georgia Press, 1989.

Introduction to Literature, Scribner Literature Series, New York, NY: Scribner and Sons Publishing Co, , 1989.

Arizona Humanities Association Journal, Vol. 6, No. 5, Spring 1987.

Mosaic, Riverside, CA: University of California at Riverside, 1986.

Album USA, (11th grade text), Glenview, IL: Scott-Foresman, 1984.

Structure & Meaning: An Introduction to Literature, Boston, MA: Houghton-Mifflin Co., 1983.

"Woman of Her Word: Hispanic Women Write, " *Revista Chicano-Riqueña,* Vol. XI, Nos. 3-4, 1983.

New Blood, Magazine #6, April 1982, Boulder, CO.

Washing the Cow's Skull, Fort Worth, TX: Prickly Pear Press, 1981.

Maize, Vol. 4, No.3-4, 1981.

Southern Exposure, Vol. IX, No. 2, 1981.

Cedar Rock, Vol. 6, No. 1, January 1981.

Metis, Austin, TX: Women & Their Work, Austin, TX, 1981.

The Third Woman, Dexter Fisher, ed., Boston, MA: Houghton-Mifflin Co., 1980.

Canto Al Pueblo, Arizona, Tucson, AZ: Post Litho Press, 1980.

Revista Chicano-Riqueña, Vol. II, No. 3, Summer 1980.

Women Working: Stories & Poems, New York, NY: McGraw-Hill, 1979.

Flor y Canto II, Austin, TX: Pajarito Publications, 1979.

Beyond Awareness Curriculum, Austin, TX: ESC Region XIII, 1979.

Canto Al Pueblo, San Antonio, TX: Penca Books, 1978.

El Quetzal Emplumece, San Antonio, TX: Mexican American Cultural Center, 1977.

Tejidos, Vol. IV, No. 4, Winter 1977.

Dále Gas, Houston, TX: Contemporary Arts Museum, 1977.

Using Contemporary Literature in the Classroom, Austin TX: Texas Circuit & Texas Commission on the Arts, 1977.

Travois, An Anthology of Texas Poets, Berkeley, CA: Thorp Springs Press, 1976.

Hembra, Austin, TX: Center for Mexican American Studies, University of Texas, 1976.

Caracol, October 1975, San Antonio, TX.

V. CHILDREN'S WORKS

Baby Coyote's Songbook and Tape, "Baby Coyote and the Old Woman," Harlingen: Baby Coyote Productions, 1995.

"Kan Kan Can," "Minnie, the Mambo Mosquito," "Mama's Birthday Present," and "Señora Gallina," in *Scott-Foresman's K-3 Reading Series*, Glenview, IL: Scott-Foresman, 1992.

"A mí me gustan los Cascarones," "La Viejita y el Bebé Coyote," "Maria del Sol," "Tacho, el Bebé Tacuache," and "El Dulcero," in *Houghton-Mifflin's K-3 Reading Series*, Boston: Houghton-Mifflin Co., in press.

Patchwork Colcha: A Children's Collection of Poems, Stories & Songs in Spanish and English, Austin, TX: Creative Educational Enterprises, Inc., 1987.

Creative Activities for Adventurous Kids, Austin, TX: Creative Educational Enterprises, Inc., 1982.

How to Make a Movie, Austin, TX: Creative Educational Enterprises, Inc., 1982

VI. CHAPTERS AND ACADEMIC ARTICLES

"Arts, Culture, and the Public Trust: San Antonio Keynote, 1990," in *Arts, Culture, and the Public Trust*, Vol. I, Austin, TX: Texas Commission on the Arts.

"Empowering Students Through Creative Writing," *Excellence in Teaching*,

February 1990.

"A University for Tomorrow's Children," *The International Journal of Humanities and Peace*, Vol. VI, No. 8, 1990.

"A Binational Wealth: Chicanas & Mexicans in Cultural Growth," *The International Journal of Humanities and Peace*, Vol. VI, No. 7, 1989

"Reyes Cárdenas," *Dictionary of Literary Biography*, Francisco Lomelí and Carl Shirley, eds., Chapel Hill, North Carolina: Gale Research Inc., 1989.

"Chicano Literature: Beyond Beginnings," in *A Gift of Tongues*, Athens, GA: University of Georgia Press, 1987.

Rural Hispanics and Developmental Disabilities: A Training Guide for Intervention, Advocacy & Parent Education, (published under a grant), Sacramento, CA: Organization for Area Boards on Developmental Disabilities, State of California, Department of Social Services, 1984

"A Review of the Second St. Poems by Beverly Silva," *La Red*, August 1984.

"From the Rio Chama to Zoot Suit: The Road to Mythical Realism," *The Pawn Review*, Vol. VI, No. 4, June 1984.

"Mujer a Mujer: Two Poets Dialogue," *Arriba*, October 1983, Austin, TX.

"Cielos," (co-authored with E.M. Bernal), *La Trompeta*, March-April 1983.

"Three Texas Women: A Poetry Critique," *Nexus*, 1982, Austin, TX.

"Chicano Writing: Beyond Beginnings," *Southern Exposure*, Vol. IX, No. 2, Summer 1981.

"The Church in Texas 1848 to 1904" and "Expansion of the Church in Texas 1904 to 1945," in *Fronteras: A History of the Latin American Church in the USA since 1513*, Vol. X of *History of the Church in Latin America*, (commissioned by the Vatican, CEHILA), San Antonio, TX: MACC/CEHILA,1983.

Some Effects of a Spanish-English Bilingual Television Series on Language Attitudes, Austin, TX: Dissertation Abstracts International, University of Texas, 1981.

"Chicano Literature," *Texas Circuit Newsletter*, Vol. II, No. 1, March 1980.

"El Cine Chicano," in *Conference Proceedings for El Primér Seminario Latinoamericano de Archivos de Imágenes en Movimiento*, Mexico City, Mexico: UNAM-UNESCO, 1980.

"La Mujer Hispana," *St. Paul Teachers' Manual for Multicultural Sex Role Development*, St. Paul, MN: St. Paul Independent School District, 1978.

VII.SCREENPLAYS/OTHER SCRIPTS/SONG LYRICS

Screenplays:

A Chance, "Sonrisas" series, 1979.

El Derecho de Estar, "Sonrisas" series, 1978.

The Choice, "Sonrisas" series, 1978.

El Curro, "Sonrisas" series, 1978.

Lágrimas del Apache, "Sonrisas" series, 1978.

The Need to Touch, "Sonrisas" series, 1978.

El Artista, "La Familia y el Respeto" package, San Antonio, TX: Southwest

Educational Development Laboratory, 1977.

Other Scripts:

Pedacitos de mi Herencia, a series of cultural commentaries, KVNA, Programa Español, 1990.

Sounds, Transportation, and 7 other scripts for "Jardín Infantíl," Mercedes Independent School District, 1982.

¿Quiénes Somos? (co-authored script to accompany slide show), San Antonio, TX: Southwest Educational Development Laboratory, 1977.

Song Lyrics:

Spanish lyrics for theme song in TV show "Misplaced Goals," "Sonrisas" series, 1978.

"Contrabando y Tamales," 1977.

CONTRIBUTORS

TERESA PALOMO ACOSTA writes, publishes, and has won awards for her poetry and stories. She and Carmen Tafolla founded conceived the first meeting of the National Institute of Chicana Writers. She counts among her credits having worked with the Texas Coordinating Board for Higher Education and having taught at St. Edwards University.

CORDELIA CANDELARIA is a professor in the Department of English at Arizona State University (formerly at the University of Colorado at Boulder). She is the author of *Seeking the Perfect Game: Baseball in American Literature* (1989), *Chicano Poetry: A Critical Introduction* (1986), a collection of poetry, *Ojo De La Cueva* (1984), *Multi-Ethnic Literature of the United States* (Edited, 1989), and has published poetry, articles and reviews in numerous other journals. Cordelia is presently a visiting professor at Stanford University (1991-92).

ALICIA CHAVEZ FRANCIS (born in San Pedro Sula, Honduras) is a student at Santa Monica College working toward a degree in Bilingual Education. She lives in Venice, California, with her eleven-year-old son, Evan, and husband, Stanley.

CATALINA GARATE was born in Tampico, Mexico. She attended the Escuela de Artes Plasticas de la Universidad de Mexico, and has her MA in Art from San Jose State University. She lives in San Jose, California, with her husband, Dr. Hector Garcia. Catalina has exhibited at the San Jose State University Gallery (exhibition title: *Rebozos*).

YOLANDA BROYLES GONZÁLEZ is a native of the Arizona/Sonora borderlands. She received her Ph.D in Germanic Studies from Stanford University. She is currently the Chair of the Chicano Studies Department and a member of the Department of Germanic, Slavic, and Asian Languages and Literatures at the University of California, Santa Barbara. Yolanda has published *The German Response to Latin American Literature* and has a book forthcoming (University of Texas Press): *El Teatro Campesino: A History of the Ensemble*. She has translated Chicano literature to the German and has published widely in performance and cultural studies areas. Yolanda also writes for the *L.A. Times* and has a new book in progress entitled *El Teatro Campesino: An Oral History*.

WOLFGANG KARRER is a professor of American Studies at the University of Osnabrück, Germany where he directs the Osnabrück Bilingual Editions of Minority Authors series.

BRYCE MILLIGAN is an award-winning newspaper book critic living in San

Antonio, Texas. He is the author of two collections of poems, hundreds of articles, three novels (for young adults) and a few plays. He was the founding editor of *Pax: A Journal for Peace through Culture* and *Vortex: A Critical Review*. A former director of literature programs at the Guadalupe Cultural Arts Center, he co-founded (with Sandra Cisneros) the Annual Texas Small Press Bookfair, now the San Antonio Inter-American Bookfair. He is currently completing a critical history entitled *Ever Radical: Tejana Writers from 1800 to the Present.*

ERNESTO PADILLA (born in Las Cruces, New Mexico, and raised in Tulare, California) received his Ph.D in Victorian literature from the University of California at San Diego. He writes both poetry and fiction and is currently working on a collection of short stories entitled *The Emperor of Ice-Cream*, stories of his boyhood barrio in Tulare. In addition, he is the editor/publisher of The Santa Monica College Press. Ernesto teaches English and American Literatures, Statistics, Algebra and Geometry.

MAYELA PADILLA was born in San Luis Obispo, California, and currently attends Santa Monica College, majoring in photography and graphic arts. Mayela is the design editor for Lalo Press.

SANDRA LUZ PEDREGAL (raised in Tijuana, Mexico) receive her BA and MA from the University of California, San Diego in Golden Age Spanish literature (thesis title: "'El asunto fue:' un estudio sobre la erudicion en La Dorotea de Lope de Vega"). Currently she is a lecturer at the School of International Relations at the University of California, San Diego. Sandra writes short stories on Tijuana border and women's issues in both English and Spanish and has been invited to take the translators' examination for the United Nations.

JOEL PÉREZ teaches at San Diego Mesa College in the English Department. He has taught English at Austin Community College, Austin, Texas, and lectured in Chicano Studies at the University of California at Riverside. He obtained his AA in English from Riverside Community College, graduating Summa Cum Laude. He received his BA in comparative literature and graduated Magna Cum Laude from the University of California at Riverside, where he also received his MA in the same area. Joel is currently working on his dissertation for the Ph.D from the University of California at Riverside. He became a member of Phi Beta Kappa in 1978 and was the recipient of the outstanding teaching assistant award at UCR. He has received numerous scholarships and fellowships, several from UCMexus for research in Mexico on scriptwriters and authors. His articles havewon literary prizes, including one published in *Bulletin*, the magazine of the California Museum of Photography. Joel has also published poems and short stories.

BEVERLY RUBIN received her A.A. from Santa Monica College and her B.A. from UCLA, *Cum Laude*. Beverly has edited and written for an entertainment trade magazine, and has edited several discographies for Joe Benson, Los Angeles disc jockey and author of *Uncle Joe's Record Guide* series, a standard for the radio broadcasting industry. While at KLOS-FM Radio, Los Angeles, she wrote public service announcements for on-air talent. Her first collection of poetry, *The Featureless*, was published in 1992. She hopes to obtain her Ph.D. in Restoration Literature with emphasis on Satire and Jonathon Swift.

ROSAURA SÁNCHEZ teaches in the Literature Department at the University of California, San Diego. She has published in the areas of literary criticism, sociolinguistics, and Chicano literature. Rosaura also writes (and has published) short stories.

DOROTHY S. (DOREY) SCHMIDT is Associate Professor in the Department of English, the University of Texas–Pan American at Edinburg — a university whose student population is 85% Chicano. She teaches multicultural literature, women's studies, and creative writing, and has been editor of *Riversedge* literary journal for more than a decade. Dorey is the recipient of a Fulbright Award as Roving Lecturer in American Studies in Norway for the academic year 1992-93, and is the author of a book of peotry entitled Lone Woman (1995).

GUADALUPE OCHOA THOMPSON received her Ph.D in Modern Languages. Formerly at University of Oklahoma (Modern Languages Department), she is presently in the Bilingual Education Department at Texas A. & I., Kingsville, Texas.